CAP'N BOB AND ME

Other books by Eleanor Berry

Tell Us a Sick One Jakey
Never Alone with Rex Malone
The Ruin of Jessie Cavendish (available in Russian)
Your Father Died on the Gallows (Two editions)
    Also translated into Russian and available in Russia
Seamus O'Rafferty and Dr Blenkinsop
Alandra Varinia, Seed of Sarah
The House of the Mad Doctors
Jaxton the Silver Boy
Someone's Been Done Up Harley
O, Hitman, my Hitman!
McArandy was Hanged under Tyburn Tree
The Scourging of Poor Little Maggie
The Revenge of Miss Rhoda Buckleshott
The Most Singular Adventures of Eddy Vernon
Take it Away, it's Red!
Stop the Car, Mr Becket!
    (formerly *The Rendon Boy to the Grave Is Gone*; available in
    Russian)
The Maniac in Room 14

find out more at www.eleanorberry.net

CAP'N BOB AND ME

The Robert Maxwell I Knew

A Ribald Black Comedy

Eleanor Berry

www.eleanorberry.net

The Book Guild Ltd
Sussex, England

The Book Guild Ltd
25 High Street
Lewes, East Sussex
BN7 2LU

First published in Great Britain 2003

Typesetting in Times by
Acorn Bookwork, Salisbury, Wiltshire

Printed in Great Britain by
Bookcraft (Bath) Ltd, Avon

A catalogue record for this book is available from
The British Library.

ISBN 1 85776 699 7

*For my brother Nicky who
introduced me to Robert Maxwell.
Also, for the actor, Bob Hoskins, who very
kindly kept me topped up with whisky,
after I'd heard about the drowning.*

Some comments.

Never Alone with Rex Malone
"A ribald, ambitious black comedy, a story powerfully told". *The Daily Mail*
"I was absolutely flabbergasted when I read it!" *Robert Maxwell*

Your Father Died on the Gallows
"A unique display of black humour which somehow fails to depress the reader." Craig McLittle. *The Rugby Gazette*
The translated words from a Moscow literary magazine: "Many Russian readers see Eleanor Berry, as a re-incarnation of 'our own beloved Dostoievsky'."

The Scourging of Poor Little Maggie
"This harrowing, tragic and deeply ennobling book, caused me to weep for two days after reading it. I had not experienced this reaction since seeing the film *The Elephant Man.*" Moira McClusky – *The Cork Evening News*

The Most Singular Adventures of Eddy Vernon
"Hardly a book for bed time." Nigel Dempster – *The Daily Mail*

Take it Away, it's Red!
"Despite the sometimes weighty portent of this book, a sense of subtle, dry and powerfully engaging humour reigns throughout its pages. The unexpected twist is stupendous." Stephen Carson – *The Carolina Sun*
"Someone told me this book was dark, but dark was hardly the word. Well, knock me over with a feather, says I!" The actress, *Sarah Miles*
"When I read *Take It Away, It's Red*, it felt like falling over a cliff on a three-wheeler." Mr Pip, Sarah Miles's chauffeur

Stop the Car, Mr Becket!
(Formerly *The Rendon Boy to the Grave is Gone.*)
"I read Eleanor Berry's book with great interest and enjoyment. She has an unusually individual authorial voice and a mordant wit which frequently had me roaring with laughter." Hunter Steele – *Ace Publications*

"Eleanor Berry's *Stop the Car, Mr Becket!* makes for fascinating and extraordinary reading, as strange and entertaining as the sixteen books which came out before it." Gaynor Evans – *Bristol Evening Post*

"A riveting, grimly humorous, erotic, unputdownable book. Ian Rosen, its dark, passionate, aggressively godless hero and randy publisher, permanently bounds from bed to bed like an out of control Labrador." Roger Taverner – *Western Daily Press*

Re: The death of Ian Rosen in the Royal Free Hospital, London. "I'm not interested in the name of the hospital he died in. All I'm concerned about is the filthy, disgusting language he used, just *before* he died!" Eleanor Berry's father

"Eleanor Berry's *Stop the Car, Mr Becket!* is a literary masterpiece." Elisa Segrave – *Journalist*.

The Maniac in Room 14
  "A side-splitter from start to finish." Guy Roberts – *Leeds Press*

1

It was the late sixties. A hunk of a man, who looked like a beautiful big black Labrador, was easing his Rolls down the Mall in the direction of Buckingham Palace. He approached the round-about where Queen Victoria, her face stern and her hand touching the royal orb, peered down upon him.

The car phone rang.

'So then, Mr Maxwell, what are you doing about your overdraft?' The caller's voice lacked the simpering whine which invariably infuriated Robert Maxwell. It was loud, confident and strident as if its owner were uninhibited and incapable of fear.

'Who the hell are you?' asked R.M., mildly irritated but impressed at the same time by the caller's boldness.

'Nicholas Berry, financial correspondent of the *Daily Telegraph*.'

'Would you like to come and see me this evening for a drink, Mr Berry? I like your journalistic style.'

The study in which R.M. met my brother Nicky for the first time was dark, sombre but tastefully decorated. They had a long talk. Nicky liked R.M. and R.M. liked Nicky.

'My birthday's coming up,' said R.M. at the end of their long discussion. 'It's on 10th June. Have you any brothers or sisters?'

'Yes, a brother and two sisters,' said Nicky, now becoming bored with the long discussion about R.M.'s overdraft.

R.M. shoved a thick cigar into his mouth, undid the top two buttons of his shirt and loosened his tie. He often did this. It never failed to excite me. He took a sip of the champagne which he and Nicky had been drinking and put his feet on an occasional table.

'Your brothers and sisters – do they live in this country?'

'My older brother is covering a story in America. My sister is in New York. My youngest sister is in London.'

R.M. took another sip of champagne and lit his cigar which had gone out.

'Your sister in London – what's her name?'

'Eleanor.'

'I'd like you to bring her to my birthday party on June 10th. Does she look like you?' he added suddenly.

'Come on Bob, that's a hard question. She's blonde but apart from that, I suppose you could say she looks like me.'

'She sounds lovely. For Christ's sake bring her along, Nicholas.'

* * *

Nicky drove me over to Headington Hill Hall. I had absolutely no idea what this was going to mean to me for the rest of my life. I had a rather ugly necklace, but had wound it round my wrist, making it look like an attractive bracelet.

Nicky introduced me to R.M. who was standing in a marquee, wearing a white towelling dressing-gown. It was so dark that I couldn't see his face properly. He was very nice and friendly and it suddenly dawned on me that he generated a livid, brutal, astonishing and overpowering sexuality. The first thing I asked of him was his permission to address him as 'Bob'.

'Yes,' he said. 'When in doubt, be brash like myself! I like your bracelet,' he added, and touched it to see what it was made of.

'How many children have you got, Bob? My mother said you had a big family.'

'Seven. I'm afraid I used to have nine. My youngest daughter, Karine, died of leukaemia in 1957 and my eldest son, Michael, died following a car accident. He was in a coma for a long time before we lost him.'

I thought I noticed his voice falter when he was giving me this information.

'I'm so sorry!'

He waved his left hand in the air a trifle dismissively as if to contain emotion. He continued: 'So Philip is my eldest son now. He's a student. Then there is Anne – she is blonde like you. After that come my twins, Isabel and Christine.'

I noticed a note of pride in his voice when he referred to 'my twins'. It was a tone of almost childlike endearment which made me feel a surge of affection towards this big man with his guttural Cossack's laugh and deep musical voice.

At the time, I had no idea that his twins had hovered between life and death in infancy and that R.M. had driven like one possessed on

2

to the pavements through the cobbled streets of Paris, looking for the nearest hospital where they were saved, only just.

'And your other children?'

'Oh yes, the others. There's my son Ian. Next in age comes Kevin and then there's Ghislaine. She is a little terror!'

The band suddenly lashed out with some heavy jazz. R.M. led me by the hand to the centre of the floor. He became very animated and twirled me round and round. He didn't know that I had suffered from vertigo all my life.

'Stop it Bob! I'm going to fall over.'

'No you're not. All I have to do is turn you the other way.' He did and it worked. 'Any better?'

'Yes. Turning the other way was a good idea.'

'All my ideas are good ones,' he said. 'And I've got another one.'

'What's that?'

'Go into the swimming hut and get into a bathing suit.' He gave the guttural laugh for which he was famous, and I had a resounding slap on the behind. 'When you've found a bathing suit, come back and see me.'

The swimming hut R.M. had referred to consisted of a sauna, a sunbed, a shower, basins and another room with a lot of bathing-suits strewn over the floor. I picked up the only one I could find which wasn't wet. It was a tight one which I suspected must have belonged to Ghislaine. I struggled to drag it on to myself. I must have looked a mess and lacked the courage to look at myself in the mirror.

'Always dress to please men and not yourself,' someone had advised me once.

I went outside to find R.M. I looked dreadful. The garment would have made the bathing suit Christine Keeler wore at Cliveden look like an outsized maternity dress.

I saw R.M. in the distance. He had wandered off to another part of the garden. Multicoloured fireworks lit up the clear star-spattered June sky, forming the words 'Happy Birthday Bob'. He seemed utterly devoid of self-consciousness or shyness. He was looking upwards at the flashing lights. I went over to him.

'Well Bob, does this bathing suit meet with your approval?'

'You look smashing!' he replied.

He picked me up without warning and carried me to the swimming-pool, laughing.

3

'What's wrong, can't you swim?'

'Oh yes,' I said, 'but I don't want to go in now.'

'Don't be such a mean old spoilsport!' I couldn't say anything to that. He threw me into the heated water and watched me swimming round the circular pool. He was laughing and chewing an unlit cigar.

I went on swimming round the pool. I got tired and swam to the edge, clutching the ground above me with both hands.

'Hullo! I know all about you, you're Eléanore, aren't you? Bob has been telling me about you. I'm Betty, Bob's wife. He told me how well he has been getting on with you. Any friend of Bob's is a friend of mine. Are you enjoying yourself?'

'Yes, thank you. I'm having a very good time. I'm pleased to meet you.'

I extended my hand to shake hands with Betty. Again, I couldn't see her face clearly in the dark but I noticed the beautiful dress she wore, together with her strong French accent. I warmed to her. I stretched out my hand, waiting for her handshake. Instead she put two barbecued sausages into my hand.

'They are fresh from the barbecue, Eléanore. Eat them before they get cold.'

What a lion of a man and what a resplendent rose of a woman! And what an honour to have become the friend of both of them! Betty knew that many women fancied R.M., but it was above her to be jealous. She was proud. In her giving and glorious life she has known neither vindictiveness, envy nor malice. All she has ever cared about has been making other people happy.

I had had quite a lot to drink by the time Nicky took me home.

'I heard about how well you hit it off with the Bouncing Czech,' said Nicky. 'I'll arrange for you to meet again if you want. He fancies you.'

I fell asleep. I had a dream that this dazzling hunk of a man was leading me by the hand to his bedroom to the accompaniment of Handel's *Saraband Duo* in D minor. Perhaps something like this happened later on. Perhaps it didn't.

* * *

It was in the late sixties that there was some ominous talk about another airport being built in Buckinghamshire. R.M. was the MP

4

for North Bucks and pressure was being put on him to be more vehement in his public speeches to condemn the airport. Trees, scattered all over Buckinghamshire, were decorated with drawings of livid, violent-looking farmers, brandishing pitchforks. Captions underneath read 'Airport! Not over our dead bodies'. I wouldn't have liked to meet one of these farmers on a dark night.

Nicky and I told the family about how much I enjoyed myself at the Maxwells'. He also told my father about the friendship which had developed so spontaneously between R.M. and me. My father was concerned about the airport. Had it been built, pretty well all the residents of Buckinghamshire would have had to leave their homes.

I have always been close to my father, a kindly, hard-working, good-humoured, but stubborn man. Once he got an idea into his head he stuck to it like a terrier with a rubber ball in its mouth and never faltered. This, I attribute to the fact that he was a Welshman.

He and I were sitting in the dining room after lunch.

'I know all about you and Bob,' he said.

'You talk as if there has been impropriety. Why did you say that?'

'I don't mean that. The reason I mentioned this is not my motive for saying what I have to say. I have nothing against your friendship.'

'Is there some kind of problem?'

'Yes. It's this business about the airport, which would mean that the whole of Buckinghamshire would be uninhabitable.'

I poured myself some more lemonade.

'I understand that. I don't really see what I can do about it.'

'I'll tell you,' my father said. 'To fight this airport, we need funds. So far, we haven't heard a word from Uncle Bob.'

I drank some more lemonade.

'Well, if you like, I don't mind going over to see him,' I said. 'I'll ask him for funds. I know he will pay if I ask him.'

My father looked at me out of the corner of his eye, half suspiciously, half amused.

'Oh, so you're as close as that, are you?'

'I never said whether I was or wasn't. I'll ring him up this afternoon and I'll invite myself over to tea. Then I'll ask him for the money. How much do you want me to ask him for?'

'Five thousand pounds.'

'Christ! Well, I'll try my best.'

My father and I left the room. I picked up the phone and dialled R.M.'s number.

'Bob, is that you?'

'Yes.'

'I will be coming over for tea with you later this afternoon, if I may.'

'Yes, of course you can, Missy. I'll tell everyone to expect you. Wear something sexy!' (I wore a tight blue denim trouser suit.)

My father's driver was called Mr Brightwell. He is dead now. Before I tell you about his memorable encounter with Robert Maxwell, I will have to say a few things about Mr Brightwell first. He looked like a gnome and had such a murderous temper, when provoked, that he would have made Ivan the Terrible seem like the chairman of a home for birds with broken wings.

I am sorry to confess that, though sickly, I was a naughty child. I can't tell you what supreme pleasure it gave me to make Mr Brightwell angry. When he was in a bait he would scream and stamp on the garage floor like Rumplestiltskin and occasionally throw a spanner at the luckless person who had upset him. He looked so funny that I enjoyed driving him into a rage.

'I wouldn't have been in your little white cotton socks for all the rice in China!' commented my sister-in-law, when I told her this.

One morning, Mr Brightwell had got ready a bowl of clean oil to pour into my father's car. I found a bucket of gravel and poured it into the bowl. His rage was indescribable.

'If you don't get out of me garridge, I'll take you by the 'and to your mother!'

'No such luck. She's gone to see her dress-maker.'

Underneath his violent temper, he had a kind heart. I got into the car to go to the Maxwells'.

'Where's Headington Hill Hall?' he asked.

'Turn right at the bottom of the drive and I'll direct you from there, Mr Brightwell.'

Mr Brightwell, though extremely friendly when not provoked, was silent throughout the journey and so was I. He took me down the sinuous, heavily ramped drive towards Headington Hill Hall.

'I understand you was only invited to tea,' said Mr Brightwell. 'I hope you're not going to dawdle. I missed *Dad's Army* last week and I'll be blowed if I am going to miss it again.'

I saw a group of men talking at the bottom of the drive just outside the house. There were at least ten of them. Because I hadn't looked at R.M.'s face properly the last time we met in the dark, I was temporarily unsure what he looked like. I approached one of the men.

'Take me to Mr Maxwell, please. Mr Robert Maxwell.'

The man did as I asked. It is not in my nature to be shy since I tend towards exhibitionism. But on this occasion I did feel rather shy and when this mood takes me over, I shout at the top of my voice and stare at the ground.

R.M. wore a beige overcoat. The hot air from his mouth formed clouds in the cold March air. For some inexplicable reason, I found this attractive.

'My father sent me here to ask you for £5000,' I said, my voice raised and my eyes still on the ground.

So far, I had not seen his face in detail.

'Who is your father and what does he want the money for?'

'For the anti-airport campaign.'

I raised my head and saw his face. A feeble March sun shone through the trees, making his jet-black eyes look hazel. His was about the most beautiful face I had ever seen, radiant, god-like and essentially masculine. When his facial muscles creased into a smile, he shone more gloriously than the sun itself.

Vertigo, which has plagued me all my life, descended on me. The trees, R.M. and the men with him, started to circle slowly round and gather speed.

I had no idea where I was when I woke up. The room was dark and the blinds were drawn. I felt sick for a while but the feeling passed. I recognized Betty who came into the room with a tray of tea and some cakes.

'What happened?' I asked.

'There is no need to worry. You were outside in the drive, talking to Bob. It was clear you hadn't had anything to eat beforehand. He said you were cold and white before you fell and that you weren't even wearing an overcoat.'

I then realized where I was and why I was there. I remembered that Mr Brightwell had implored me not to be too long because he wanted to watch *Dad's Army*.

Betty sat and talked to me, first in English, then in French. She said I was welcome to stay in her house at any time. Then she

7

turned off the light and told me to rest. She said R.M. would be in to see me later. He came in within about 20 minutes.

'Well then, Miss,' he began. (Sometimes he called me 'Missy', sometimes 'Pussycat' and occasionally 'Basso Profundo' due to my deep voice.)

'I am not ill, I just fell over, that's all.'

He looked puzzled and suggested calling a doctor. My thoughts went immediately to Mr Brightwell's wrath due to missing *Dad's Army*. Because I was older, I was no longer amused by his tantrums.

'There is a driver outside waiting for me,' I said. 'He'll be furious if he misses *Dad's Army*.'

Bob brushed a stray lock of black hair from his forehead.

'Fuck *Dad's Army*!' he said, his voice raised. 'I've had the rare pleasure of meeting you twice and apart from your good looks, I don't know anything about you. I know about your family but I don't know anything about you as a person. What are your interests?'

'Russian music, Russian literature, piano playing and the Communist Party.'

At that time, I was a dotty, starry-eyed Communist and I told him, not without considerable pride, that I was a member of the Communist Party.

'Have you been to Russia?'

'Yes, I went there last winter.'

'With whom?' he demanded suddenly.

'I went alone.'

'Alone?' He looked as if he had swallowed a bee. I couldn't understand his astonishment.

'Yes, why not? I do a lot of things alone.'

He stared me in the face. Had I not been lying down, I might have fainted again.

'Christ, I have never seen such guts, but you are scared of your driver's rage if he misses bloody *Dad's Army*!'

'I am not scared. He missed it last week as well. The only thing I am scared of in life is illness.'

He ignored this, and tilted his head backwards, something he always did when he was surprised or being lied to.

'Wait a minute, Miss,' he said, 'I have something to show you.'

Five minutes later, he came in with a pile of beautifully bound

Russian books by Pushkin, Gorky and Gogol. How I wished I spoke more Russian then! I made up my mind that I would teach myself the language, to delight and excite him.

'Accept this as my esteem for your beauty, your guts and your company.'

'They are all beautiful. You *are* "kind"!'

'I am not kind!' he said with peculiar certainty. 'Would you like me to read to you a little?'

'But what about that driver outside?'

'Fuck the driver outside! What would you like me to read?'

'Tatyana's conversation with her nanny from *Yevgeni Onegin*.'

'I admire the resolution with which you make up your mind.'

He opened the book in the right place and read the sad verses about a woman's unrequited love.

'Will you sign these books, Bob?' He took out a pen and did as he was asked. 'To Eleanor with admiration.' I suddenly noticed he was left-handed and, without knowing why, I felt another surge of excitement, maybe because I knew him to be different from others.

'Now for the cheque for your dad.' He wrote it out and put it into an envelope. I didn't see the amount.

'Right, Miss, it's time you got up. Then we can have tea. Perhaps your driver would like to join us. What's his name?'

'Mr Brightwell.'

'Mr Lightweight – did you say?'

I had uncontrollable giggles.

'What's so funny?'

'No, it's Brightwell, not Lightweight.'

It was already dark. Mr Brightwell was sitting in my father's navy-blue, somewhat hearse-like Ford estate, smoking cigarettes and looking at a tabloid paper showing photographs of naked women.

R.M. banged peremptorily on the window. I must point out that he related far more easily to women than members of his own sex, so his handling of the highly peppery Mr Brightwell was the opposite of the way he treated me.

'You there, sitting in your vehicle, looking at pictures of naked women,' boomed R.M., as if Mr Brightwell were sitting 50 yards away. 'What are you reading? What have you got there?'

An expression of rage clouded over Mr Brightwell's gnome-like face. I got the giggles.

9

'Mind your own flippin' business, sir!'

R.M. ignored the remark.

'I'd like you to come into my house and have tea with me and my wife,' said R.M. His words sounded more like a command than a social invitation.

'Your name's Mr Lightweight, isn't it?' said Bob (tongue in cheek).

I thought Mr Brightwell was about to expire with apoplexy, so Draconian was his rage.

'No, it isn't!' he bellowed. 'My name is Mr BRIGHTWELL.' He spat it out, letter by letter.

Mr Brightwell's appalling temper worsened and he went purple in the face, fanatically taking off his cap and putting it on again. He turned his head towards R.M., his eyes almost coming out of their sockets. I struggled desperately to keep a straight face.

'I'll have you know that I have served the Berry family, man and boy and the Smith family before that!' he bellowed in a homicidal rage. 'It was my privilege to groom Lord Birkenhead's* horses!'

R.M. appeared puzzled by his aggression and must have wondered why an invitation to tea had made another man so livid.

'Bugger what you did to Lord Birkenhead's horses!' said R.M., this time very impatiently. 'Get out of your vehicle and come into my house and have tea with us. Eleanore said you were keen on *Dad's Army*.'

Mr Brightwell put his cap on and threw his paper on to the floor of the car. He put out his cigarette and got out very hesitantly, staring furiously at R.M. as he moved. He walked slowly into the house with his head lowered as if he were walking behind his mother's hearse.

R.M. led us into a room with Empire furniture, a harp and a piano. Mr Brightwell was introduced to Betty to whom he was stiffly courteous. She offered him some cakes that she had made herself and which he refused, and tea which he accepted, sitting on the edge of his chair throughout.

R.M. asked Mr Brightwell a number of inoffensive questions,

---

*Lord Birkenhead, known better as F.E. Smith, was the Author's maternal grandfather. Barrister, wit, statesman and Lord Chancellor, he died in 1930, long before the Author was born.

delivered with the arresting and startling intonation characteristic of him, and was answered with monosyllables. To this day I have never been able to work out whether Mr Brightwell's answers were due to rage that he might miss *Dad's Army* or atypical reticence.

'When does *Dad's Army* start, Betty?' asked her husband.

'In about 15 minutes. I'd like to see it as well.'

'That's good. Our guest likes it and would like to see it. You'll stay and watch it here, won't you?' said R.M.

Mr Brightwell seemed self-conscious. 'That's very nice of you but Eleanor's father will be wanting her back.'

We got up to go. I said goodbye to both the Maxwells and had a nice kiss on the mouth from R.M. I noticed that Betty said nothing and seemed not to object to this.

Mr Brightwell walked out first. R.M. took me aside.

'Christ, that driver of yours is a scary fellow! I wouldn't like to meet him alone on a dark night.'

That set me off again; my giggles were uncontrollable.

'It doesn't take much to get you going,' said R.M. 'You're a bit batty, aren't you?'

'You don't understand how comical he is when he gets in a rage,' I said. 'When I was small, I used to pour gravel into his bowl of clean oil, just to see his furious face and get him to throw a spanner at my head.'

'Missy, you're bloody barmy!'

On the way home I tried to break the stony silence.

'What did you think of Mr Maxwell, Mr Brightwell?'

'No comment!' he barked.

It was fairly late by the time I got home. My mother was upstairs. My father was waiting for me, sitting by the fire.

'Have you got the money? What took you so long?'

I passed the sealed envelope to my father. When he opened it, he seemed irritated.

'This amount falls cheekily short of the £5000* I asked you to get from Bob,' he said.

---

*The amount did indeed fall short of £5000 but though the Author knows what the exact amount was, she refrains from indulging in malicious gossip and will not disclose what was written on the cheque.

'I can't help that. I went over there, didn't I? It was very nice of him to give you any money at all.'

My father looked puzzled.

'You still didn't tell me why you were away for so long. Did any impropriety take place between you?'

'No.'

I fondled the signed books under my arm with pride. They, and not the money, were the trophies of my expedition.

'I was away for so long because I made the mistake of looking the man in the eye. It's true I had met him before in the dark but I didn't see his face, then. In daylight, he was so extraordinarily good-looking that I fainted and I had to be put to bed.'

'You fainted?'

'Yes. I inherit occasional fainting attacks from you.'

'That's right. Blame your poor father!'

He saw that I was becoming irritated and he must have felt that his words were inappropriate.

'All the same, it was very sporting of you to do what you did, even though you didn't get as much money as I would have liked.'

I rang R.M. up and thanked him.

'You have a permanent invitation to my house,' he said. 'You can stay as long as you want whenever you want. Betty and I look upon you as being one of our children. I also think you're bloody sexy!'

2

I suffered from an illness diagnosed as schizophrenia in my teens. The condition was extremely unpleasant. In later life, I have suffered from OCD, known as 'obsessive compulsive disorder'. I am also a manic-depressive.

Part of my ill health in my teens was caused by an inner conflict about my having joined the Communist Party. I began to lose faith in its ideals when I read about Russian intellectuals being sent to labour camps.

One of the most unpleasant things about Communism was a memory of a visit to Moscow. I saw a play about the Russian Revolution, called *Shestoi Illyoolia*. When the actor, playing the part of Felix Dershinsky (the Head of Lenin's secret police, the NKFD) swaggered onto the stage, many members of the audience, rose to their feet, cheering and clapping. That wasn't the only thing which troubled me. I became morbidly obsessed by Russian literature and its macabre, hopeless, desolate tones. I was so curious that I couldn't stop myself reading these books.*

The straw which broke the camel's back, where my loss of faith in Communism was concerned (sorry about the cliché), was a visit to East Berlin. In his Manifesto, Lenin had said 'We'll build gold latrines for the workers!' I went to the lavatory in East Berlin. When I pulled the chain, the ballcock came away in my hand and the tank crashed to the floor.

I didn't want to believe what I read about Communism in the newspapers, however. One morning, my mother arranged to meet me in Aldo Bruno's, an upmarket hairdresser's in Mayfair. I was about 16 at the time. I had a bundle of rolled-up newspapers under my arm. The top newspaper on the pile was the *Daily Worker*.

---

*For a more lighthearted account of this matter, see Berry's article in the April 2001 edition of *The Oldie*, when she visits a film set and pesters Herbert Lom about Russian literature, causing him to crack up and forget his lines.

Everyone knows it is a Communist newspaper.

I greeted my mother, sat down beside her and started reading it. Hairdressers stared at us, giggling. They knew that I was both annoying and embarrassing my mother.

Had she not made so much noise, expressing her shock that I was reading a Communist newspaper in a Mayfair hairdresser's (which is frequented by film stars, the aristocracy and newspaper proprietors' wives among others), she probably wouldn't have attracted so much attention to what I was reading.

Her voice was even louder and deeper than mine. She picked the paper up and waved it in the air.

'Where in the world did you get this?'

'I bought it,' I said.

'Why did you buy it?'

'Because I like it.'

'Why do you like it?'

'Why?' I said loudly. 'I like its content, I like its editorials and I like its reasoning.'

Aldo Bruno himself, who owned the hairdresser's, allowed his mouth to gape open like a goldfish about to bite the dust. He appeared to lack a sense of humour. His scissors fell from his hand, onto the floor.

'I can see she won't be coming in here again,' he said.

'You do see I have an awful lot to put up with,' said my mother, her voice uncharacteristically low, like a Catholic making confession.

It was when my mother and I were walking across the street to her car that she began to take off. First, she spoke (loudly enough to be heard in Bayswater) about farmers under Stalin being collectivized and the horror of the soviet labour camps.

Flabbergasted passers-by formed a circle around us to listen to her articulate condemnation of the perils of Russian Communism. Suddenly, she added as if as an afterthought:

'Do you realize Lady Glendevon, the Marchioness of Salisbury and Lady Rothermere were all in there today? You've made a laughing stock of us both!'

My mother turned her embarrassment into a joke, later on, at a family gathering. Her narrative was so distorted that the incident became surreal. Disgruntled hairdressers were accounted for as fainting in droves. Even imaginary ambulances were described, screeching to a halt, before picking up traumatized aristocrats in curlers.

* * *

'Do you mind if we have Bob to lunch on Sunday?' This was my brother, Nicky asking. 'Besides, I need to find out why he wants to buy the *News of the World*.'

'Certainly not this Sunday,' said my mother. 'Adelaide Jesus has got to go to Barbados for a funeral.'

'Who the hell's Adelaide Jesus?'

'She's the cook. Didn't you know that?'

'No. I've often seen a woman working in the kitchen but I had no idea she had a bonkers name like Adelaide Jesus!'

'Adelaide Jesus is no stranger a name than Nicholas Berry,' said my mother angrily.

'Can't we hire someone while she's away?'

'No. All we've got is Mary, a 72-year-old dear who sometimes comes in from the village. She's just about capable of boiling an egg,' said my mother, adding, 'One can't give Robert Maxwell a boiled egg for lunch. He's so peculiar and sensitive, he might totally misconstrue the situation! Get the man over the following Sunday.'

'I'll ring him up,' said Nicky.

'Yes, do do that. After all, he has been very kind to Eleanor, giving her all those books like that.'

R.M. came over, minus Betty but with his identical twin daughters, Isabel and Christine. He wore a fur hat and trench-like overcoat. He sat next to my mother at lunch and I sat on his other side.

Suddenly, he turned to me. I was feeling shy which he sensed. He wanted to bring me into the conversation.

'Are you keen on opera?'

'Yes, some operas. *Carmen*'s my favourite and I like *La Traviata* and *The Magic Flute*.'

'I admire the extent of your knowledge. Are you interested in politics?'

'She's a Communist, you know. She needs to read the *Daily Worker* every day, just as a Chinaman needs rice!' said my mother.

'I know she's a Communist. She told me when I last saw her,' said R.M.

15

'And she's a card-carrying member of the Communist Party. She carries bouquets of flowers to the Russian Embassy on Lenin's birthday every year,' said my mother.

R.M. looked approvingly at me but I couldn't understand why. Perhaps he thought I was eccentric, and he had a penchant for eccentric women.

'Christ, what amazing guts!' he exclaimed.

* * *

It was not long afterwards that illness struck me down. Apart from confusion about Communism and an agonizing preoccupation with Russian literature, it was precipitated by about twenty different causes, none of which I intend to strain myself, or my readers, by listing. I am, however, cured. My compulsory hospitalization was brought about by the following singularly trivial incident:

A friend called Peter Van Praagh* gave me a gold cigarette case for my birthday. The only thing he left out was an engraving. I had a good idea. There's an old Russian song that I like which has the advantage of a chorus being interchangeable with English words:

> *Nye zhivoi v styeppi, chellovyek lezhit.*
> *Okolo myotvovo voron kruzhit* [in Cyrillic letters].

The English words for the chorus are:

> *In the steppe a dead man lies.*
> *Round the man a raven flies.*

---

*Peter Van Praagh: A very dear childhood friend. He was the model for Joseph Slandisch in *Your Father Died on the Gallows*. He took his life in March 1988 but had the courtesy to purchase fifteen copies of my *Never Alone with Rex Malone* first.

Of further note is the fact that *Your Father Died on the Gallows* is now available in Russia, and enjoying popularity there. Although not relevant to the matter in hand, a Russian journal reviewing it stated, generously, that I was 'almost a reincarnation of our own beloved Dostoievsky.' I know R.M. would have been proud of me!

16

My tastes veer towards the macabre. I went to a jeweller, being ignorant of his amateurishness, while waiting for a train at Paddington Station on my way to stay with the Maxwells. The thin, scruffy, bearded man standing behind the counter was unattractive and unfriendly, but I decided not to go anywhere else.

'Yes?' said the man.

This made me hostile.

'See this gold cigarette case I've got here?'

The man scratched his unkempt beard.

'What about it?' he asked in a taciturn tone.

'Here is a piece of paper with writing on it. I've written the words in capitals and I'd like them in italics, if you would, please.

'There's another thing I want to point out to you. The word 'steppe' is not spelt S-T-E-P but S-T-E-P-P-E.'

'That's bloomin' stupid,' he said. ''Course it's S-T-E-P!'

I did not feel like lecturing the man on Russian literature or geography.

'I've just told you that it's the way I want it spelt,' I said.

I was about to put the cigarette case on the counter but he beat me to it by snatching it from my hand.

'There's no need to snatch it,' I said.

I walked out. I felt happy that day because I was on my way to see the Maxwells, and when it was my birthday I was always allowed to sit on R.M.'s right and be the centre of his attention. Some people feared doing this because of his sudden way of asking penetrating questions. It never bothered me, though, because I had learnt that he liked his guests, particularly women, to bark at him in reply. Sometimes, when women barked at him, he would collapse in hysterical giggles like a child. If a woman barked at him too harshly, however, he would go into an angry silence. I caused him to do the latter three times later in his life, and when I did I felt guilty and unhappy afterwards.

These were some of the thoughts passing through my mind as I sat in a coffee bar at Paddington, waiting for the jeweller to do the engraving. For some reason, the strong coffee deepened my hostility towards him and I became suspicious. I feared he had damaged my property. I went into the shop.

'Is it ready?'

He slapped the cigarette case on the counter.

'Fifteen quid,' he said and stretched out his hand, palm

upwards, like a down-market debt-collector.

'When I see it, you'll get your money.'

I picked it up and examined it under the Anglepoise lamp, precariously balanced at the edge of the counter.

He had done what I had told him not to do. He had engraved 'step' and had also carved the quotation in ordinary letters when I had asked for italics.

I don't know what I did next, but I realized I had flown into a rage. I hit him on both sides of his face. He called the police, wasting their valuable time.

I usually have the gift of the gab and realized I had to get my word in first if I was to get to the Maxwells for lunch. I went towards the policeman looking older than his colleague. I chose the most flowery and verbose language possible to bore my listeners.

'Good morning, sir,' I said, 'I'm ever so sorry to have called you and your colleague out on this nice May morning but first, I must emphasize one very important point: I'm not fully cognizant of how familiar you are with Russian literature and geographical factors pertaining thereto. In Russia, particularly in Eastern Russia, there are plains interspersed occasionally by tall, gaunt, mottled-trunked birch trees, which are referred to as the Steppes.'

The policeman gaped at me halfwittedly. He opened his mouth to speak but no words came. I was afraid he might interrupt me so I continued.

'The extent of your knowledge about the Steppes is, I regret, unknown to me, but if you do not know about either them or the poetry relating to them, I would be most indebted to you for allowing me to familiarize you with another extremely important point.

'The word "steppe", when describing the Russian Steppes, which I have already touched on in passing, is not spelt S-T-E-P, as a person unfamiliar with Russian literature and geography might think. It is spelt S-T-E-P-P-E. Now that I have furnished you with this reasonably unimportant but necessary information, I will inform you of the precise circumstances leading to your encounter with me.'

'I don't want to hear all this pompous, potty talk!' snapped the officer. 'You struck this gentleman. Why?'

'He tried to get violent. I defended myself. He also swindled me and damaged my property. I'm bored with this incident. I've got

18

to catch my train.'

'Where do you think you're going?'

'To Robert Maxwell's house,' I said quietly.

'No, you aren't. You've committed an offence. We are charging you with assault.'

'A woman's got the right to defend herself against a violent thug, hasn't she?'

The odious man told his side of the story, deliberately exaggerating throughout. As is sometimes the case, when even minor assaults are committed, I was 'sectioned'. Two psychiatrists signed a bogus form to indicate I was 'mad' and after that I was incarcerated. A thick needle was pushed into my arm while white-coated Health Service employees held me steady. The needle contained a substance called Chlorpromazine which induces suicidal depression and turns you into a vegetable.

Once I was immobilized, and unable to struggle, they tried to take details from me. I said I was 21 as opposed to 17 and that my parents, whom I didn't want informed, were touring round America and there was no way of getting hold of them. I gave my brother Nicky's name as my next of kin.

My mind came to a halt. I had no feelings at all. I could neither laugh nor cry and I forgot it was my birthday. I had no idea how long they had kept me in a horrific orange-walled cubicle on my own, or how long I had been subjected to the loneliness my wicked captors imposed on me.

Among the things the Chlorpromazine did to me was to give me hallucinations. When I opened a drawer in the tiny cubicle, I saw a decapitated baby in it. Once, when I was taken to the bathroom, I saw a hanged man covered in blood.

When Nicky came to see me, my first reaction was one of relief, but the depression caused by the Chlorpromazine injections made me unaware of reality and destroyed my will to ask him to get me out.

The misery increased and got worse each day. The nurses, instructed by the psychiatrists, continued to fill me with Chlorpromazine and decided I should have electric shock therapy for the depression it caused. It did not occur to them to work out what was causing it. The electric shocks made it worse. I have done a lot of research and know a great deal about mental illness, through having worked with patients, as well as having been a part-time Agony Aunt for three years. Electric shock treatment is a grey area. It can only be used on deeply depressed patients. In these circumstances, it is said to have a 50-50 recovery rate. If a patient's depression is drug-induced, and hence artificial, electric shock treatment is extremely dangerous. It can push the patient into 'catatonia' (meaning he/she can't move, speak, sit or stand). If the treatments are stopped, the patient might eventually recover. If too many are given, the patient becomes like a road-accident victim. He/she will turn into a vegetable forever.

I began to work out a plan to take my life. Somehow, the nurses were aware of this. For several days, they took it in turns to sit with me day and night to make sure I didn't commit suicide.

I had no idea what was going on outside. At about 1.30 p.m. on 6th May, Nicky received a peremptory call from Robert Maxwell.

'Where the hell's that sister of yours, Nicholas? We're giving a lunch for her and she hasn't turned up. Bloody hell! I've been looking forward to seeing her and I've got to go to Moscow later this afternoon for a week.'

Nicky tried to explain the situation as delicately as possible.

'Sorry, Bob, but something very odd happened this morning at Paddington Station. Apparently my sister got into an argument with a man about the spelling of a word on a cigarette case. My sister assaulted him.'

'What the hell are you talking about, Nicholas?'

'My sister had to go to hospital.'

'You mean the man harmed her?'

'No. She attacked him. I can't give details, now. When do you get back from Moscow?'

'In a week. Is she injured?'

'No. But I'll have to talk to you urgently when you come back.'

'Why do you say "urgently", having said she's not injured?'

'I'm afraid my sister may be mentally ill.'

'Mentally bloody ill? No, she isn't.'

'She's in a hospital. Perhaps you're the only person who can help her. The psychiatrists are making her worse.'

'Listen, Nicholas, I'll call you as soon as I'm back. Leave a number where I can get you. Give me the numbers of the fucking psychiatrists involved. Do her parents know?'

'No.'

'That's not important. I'll sort it out myself. Look after her when I'm away.'

To this day, I have no idea where this hospital was. It may have been in North London somewhere, because 20 years later when travelling through North London, I had a sudden unexplained attack of misery and palpitations.

The switchboard at the hospital was jammed with calls from Moscow. R.M. demanded to speak to the psychiatrists, who avoided him. Although he was medically untrained, I think he was psychic. This could have been inherited from his adored mother, Hannah Hoch. When he was four years old, she predicted that he would be internationally famous one day. Somehow, he knew that a combination of high dose anti-psychotic drugs (in the form of Chlorpromazine) and electric shock treatment would not cure, but kill, if prolonged. After I had had about five treatments, I had lost my memory and had sunk further still until I reached catatonia.

Nicky rang R.M. on his car phone while he was coming back from Heathrow Airport. He had been to the hospital and recognized my state.

'My sister's worse, Bob! The GP says he doesn't know as much as the psychiatrists and has to be guided by them.'

'Christ, Nicholas! Calm down. Remind me of the name of this fucking asylum.'

Nicky told him.

'Who's this fucking GP?'

'A certain Dr Carl Heinz Goldman.' He gave him Goldman's number.

Carl Heinz Goldman (now deceased) was a well-known, controversial figure who kept a high profile in the élitist Harley Street community. He was devastatingly attractive and spoke with a seductive, guttural Leipzig accent. He was a compulsively randy rake about town.

He was a moody, passionate, warm and exceptionally melancholy man which made him even more attractive. I had been in love with him for some time and invented gynaecological diseases as an excuse to lie on his leather-studded consulting couch and receive his internal examinations. He has appeared in some of my books as 'Dr Festenstein'. Because he is a recurrent character, I never kill him off.

R.M. rang Goldman. The randy doctor was astounded by the excitable publisher who spoke to him in an arresting, extremely confrontational manner and accused him of allowing me to be

21

'sectioned'. He also told him he knew 'fuck all' about medicine.

Apparently during the conversation, Goldman had called Maxwell a 'crook', and Maxwell had called Goldman a 'quack'. 'Oh, I say, they were both absolutely right!' commented some cheeky Sloane Ranger, months after the much-talked-about, fiery argument between the two slick, East European sex sirens.

It was only after I'd left the hospital that R.M. said, irritably, 'I just wasn't able to hit it off with that fucking doctor!'

Interestingly, the latter also complained to me.

'Are you in love with Robert Maxwell?' he asked.

'I think I am.'

'Pity! Who the hell does that bastard think he is? Why doesn't he look more to the Board of Trade Report about his dishonest dealings? He should keep his own business in order, instead of telling me how to practise medicine. I don't interfere with his butchered finances and publishing activities, so I don't want him pestering me again!' ranted Goldman. His livid words were hardly decipherable.

*   *   *

R.M. rang Nicky again, after his contretemps with Goldman.

'Nicholas!' he shouted.

'Yes. What's going on?'

'I got onto that Goldman fellow. He sounded a pretty slippery, shady character, unfit to be in charge of a registered Harley Street practice. I'm going straight to the hospital. I'll sort Eleanor myself.' He hung up.

R.M.'s driver's name was Mr Hoppitt. That wasn't his nickname, it was his actual name! He did not take offence easily and had a sense of humour, which is why R.M. kept him. I heard later that R.M. got out a map and directed Hoppitt to the hospital. He always liked him to drive fast and Hoppitt must have screeched to a halt outside, judging by the skid marks in the gravel.

R.M. strode into the hospital, wearing a white flannel suit and a coal-miner's cloth cap. I had been wheeled into the operating theatre once more, to be brought closer to death.

R.M. found his way to the theatre and rattled straight in. Someone had put two electrodes on each side of my head and was about to turn on the machine. I pleaded with them not to turn the

22

machine on, but they said they'd been told to. I was *compos mentis* enough to see R.M. coming up to the machine. Someone was about to give me an anaesthetic. Two figures shrouded in gowns, looked at him.

'You're not scrubbed up!' shouted one of them.

'I order you not to turn that fucking machine on!' said R.M.

They were mesmerized. He extended his hand to me. 'Come on, you. Off that table! Hold me by the arm.'

The staff did nothing. It was as if they were under hypnosis.

'Come on. Try to walk a bit faster. Where are your things?' asked R.M.

'Small orange cubicle by entrance.'

'Why aren't you using the definite article?'

We went into the cubicle.

'Do you mean they locked you up in here?'

'Yes.'

'Bastards! Come on, take that hideous green thing off and put on your clothes. You're all right with me. I'll face the wall. I'm not ready to seduce you yet!'

I got dressed. My hair was tangled. R.M. tried to brush it but pulled so much I had to tell him to stop. I was dizzy and sat down and put my head between my legs. Then I noticed the smallness of R.M.'s hands. They were delicate like a woman's. I couldn't understand how such small, gentle-looking hands could wield the physical strength of a Colossus. I was also struck by the extreme sweetness of his breath.

It was then that I knew one thing and one thing only. This beautiful-looking man was God.

I was reminded of an essay by Gorky about his conversations with Tolstoi. He stated, 'I, who do not believe in God, thought this man was God-like.'

He walked me towards the entrance. I kept falling over.

'Help me, Bob. It's the drugs.'

'You should never have got yourself in here. You attacked a man at Paddington Station on 6th May, I heard. Douglas someone or other, they said his name was. When the police came, you lectured them about the bloody Russian Steppes. What the hell had you taken?'

'I can't remember the incident at all.'

'It was your birthday – you were on your way to Betty and me.'

23

'Oh yes, I remember going to the station. Nothing else.'

He wasn't all that interested in the incident, I didn't think. He put out his arm (we were out in the drive).

'Hold on to me and come with me.'

If it hadn't been for the fact that I was still very ill, I would have found the situation comical. Burly male nurses and sadistic beady-eyed female nurses stared transfixed at R.M. as if they had seen a vision. They were terrified of him. Regardless of my black state of mind, I looked at him in wonder, fascinated by his power to petrify others just by looking at them.

I held his arm with both hands to steady myself and kept my eyes lowered.

'*Yea though I walk through the valley of the shadow of death, I will fear no evil: for thou art with me; thy rod and thy staff comfort me,*' I said out loud.

'Shut up! I've been travelling all night. I don't want a load of the Scriptures thrown at me now!'

He guided me to the car.

A number of factors caused R.M.'s actions to be entirely legal. First, one of the examining psychiatrists at the police station was unqualified. Second, hitting a man's face is not severe enough to merit being sectioned. Perhaps it was my deliberately pompous verbal delivery to the baffled policeman, which invited it. Third, neither the psychiatrist, nor the man posing as one, contacted my GP, Dr Goldman, to say what was going on, until R.M. confronted him. They failed to tell him I was receiving Chlorpromazine and shock treatment. Finally, as I gave my age as being over 18, I should have been issued with a consent form to give signed permission to receive any treatment. Added to that, there was never a consultant in the operating theatre, only two junior doctors and a trainee.

The cheerful Mr Hoppitt sprang nimbly from the Rolls and opened the back door while R.M. continued to hold me steady. He gave me a slap on the behind and pushed me in.

'We'll go to my house in Fitzroy Square,' he said, 'and can you get a move on.'

'I'll do my best, Mr Maxwell. I can't do more than that.'

Hoppitt could be a stickler for observing the speed limit. I could feel R.M.'s frustration beside me.

Suddenly, he hit Hoppitt on the back of the head with a rolled

24

up copy of the *Financial Times*. This was something he always did to drivers he thought were driving too slowly. Hoppitt was in a 30 m.p.h. zone. He increased his speed to 55 m.p.h. and was hauled into the side.

'Would you please get out of your car, sir. I'll see your licence while you're at it,' said the policeman.

Hoppitt got out and did as he was told. R.M. also got out and eased himself into the driver's seat.

'Sorry, officer,' he said, 'I'm in a bastard of a hurry. You'll have to sort this out with my driver.'

He drove off leaving Hoppitt with the policeman. I got the giggles.

'What are you laughing at?' he asked.

'I like your style,' I said.

We drove on in silence until we came to a traffic jam. R.M. moved over to the right-hand side of the road and crashed along with his hand on the horn.

The telephone rang. I could hear a crisp female voice telling him there was a call from Rome. R.M. spoke at length in French to the caller. His conversation was entirely about high finance, a subject which bores me. It was evident from his conversation that things weren't going the way he wished. Eventually, he hung up.

'So how's Rome, Bob?' I asked.

He looked strained and irritated.

'Rome stands where Rome stood, on the Tiber!'

The rest of the journey was in silence.

His house in Fitzroy Square was dark and gloomy with sombre, oak-coloured panelling and poor lighting.

'You could do with a glass of champagne, Missy.'

He gave a spectacular wolf-whistle and a Filipino maid entered the room.

'I'd prefer a Coca-Cola, Bob,' I said.

'Come on! I can't be doing with people who don't drink alcohol. The more you drink when you're young, the stronger the walls of your liver get!'

'You're right. I would rather have champagne.'

When the glass was passed to me, I drank it in one gulp in an effort to disperse the gloom caused by the treatment.

'That's more like it, Missy.'

'I might as well have another.'

He filled my glass to the brim. I drained it in one go. I could feel the depression shifting.

'I'll have another, if I may. I'm beginning to feel better.'

'All right but I'm only going to give you half. I'm taking you out to lunch and I don't want you passing out.'

He drove me to a busy restaurant somewhere in the City. We sat on the same side of the table. He ordered more champagne.

'Let's see how strong a head you've got. But don't knock it back in one go, otherwise you'll be sick.' He poured the champagne into my glass and told the waiter to bring two steaks.

'Let's have the truth, then,' he said suddenly before the lunch arrived. 'How did you really come to be so stupid as to have yourself put into that bloody hospital? I want your own version of events.'

'It was a trivial thing, really. A jeweller at Paddington Station stole a gold cigarette case I'd been given. I wanted something engraved on it and he refused to give it back to me. We had a fight and things went on from there.'

'You shouldn't be smoking anyway. It's bloody dangerous. I've had a lung removed because of it. To get back to what happened, what things went on from where, for Christ's sake?'

'My memory's not so good because of the drugs still in my system. I was put into the hands of a couple of bent shrinks.'

'Shrinks? What the hell are they?'

'Sorry, I meant psychiatrists.'

'You were a fool to get involved with them. Here you are, looking ill and in a bloody awful state, wasting your life.'

His booming voice reverberated throughout the crowded restaurant. Diners turned round to stare at us and I was proud to be seen with R.M. He went on just as loudly.

'You've got looks. You've got brains. You've joined the Communist Party and even had the guts to go to Russia alone. Why don't you come and work for me? You could even move into my house, and I'd look after you.'

I was feeling better but certainly not at all well. The idea of committing myself to working for this somewhat exacting task-master gave me claustrophobia.

'I don't want to make a spontaneous decision,' I said. 'You'll have to give me time to think it over. Besides, I'm not quite fit enough to work yet. My psychiatrists say I've got schizophrenia.'

'What's wrong with that? Bugger what your psychiatrists say, if you'll excuse my soldier's language.' Then in a much quieter tone he added gently, 'I've got schizophrenia too, Ellie. I've had it since I was about your age. It isn't a serious disease.'

'That's not right. It's terribly serious. Why haven't you been to a doctor about it?'

'I don't believe in bloody doctors!' he replied, angrily. 'I've learnt to live with it.'

'What caused you to get it?'

'It was my past,' he said abruptly.

I looked sideways at him and saw that he looked haunted and disturbed, as if he had been hit on a raw nerve.

'I'm sorry to hear that,' I said.

At that time, I had no idea that his family, who were Jewish Czechoslovaks, had been taken to Auschwitz and gassed. Among them was his mother on whom he doted with a love almost on a par with that of Paul Morel for his mother, in *Sons and Lovers*. Among them, too, was his grandfather who had taught him his bargaining ability and shrewd business sense. This man was the father figure in his life. He didn't get on with his own father, with whom he apparently had an utterly dreadful relationship. I will mention this matter again, later on in this book.

R.M. sat in a brooding silence lasting about ten minutes. I drank more champagne because I felt the melancholia, inflicted on me by the hospital staff, returning.

'Waiter! Two Turkish coffees!'

The other diners, who obviously didn't have anything better to do than gape at a couple of eccentrics, all stopped talking.

The waiter brought the coffee to the table in a container but forgot to bring any sugar. The extra champagne made me uninhibited.

'I want sugar, Bob.'

'You're right to say "I want" instead of "please may I have". It puts others in awe of you and you can get what you want more quickly. A person too timid to say "I would like" gets nowhere. No doubt you've been taught otherwise but I'm rougher because I've had it rough. Waiter! Sugar!'

Sugar was brought to the table. It's quite a helpful agent in treating melancholia so I put four spoonfuls into the small cup provided.

'Christ, you've got a sweet tooth!' said R.M.

I sensed that his brooding mood had passed. I took his hand in mine which he appeared to like.

'Thanks for lunch, Bob. Where do you want to take me now?'

'To my house in Oxford. My wife Betty and I are going to look after you until you are more under control. Nicholas is coming to dinner tonight. I'm sure you'll like that.'

'You've been so kind to me,' I said.

'I'm not kind! You've got something about you that I like and admire.'

'Oh! What's that?' I asked.

'I'll tell you what. You've got looks, you've got guts, and you don't take any shit from anyone!'

I felt a sudden glorious elixir. I knew that I worshipped R.M. with every inch of my being.

'I can tell by my association with you that there will be nothing in life you want that you won't get. Just demand it and it will be yours. You've got a loud, deep voice, designed to scare the wits out of anyone. I will have to call you "Basso Profundo". On top of that, you're as stubborn as a mule!'

'That's because my family are Welsh originally but they all moved to London, long before I was born. The Welsh are a stubborn lot.'

R.M. didn't appear to take this in.

'I look upon you as a daughter. I also find you physically attractive,' he said.

3

My head gradually got better over the weeks when the toxins disappeared from my blood. I wasn't feeling well the first night in the Maxwells' house but Nicky's presence at dinner, combined with his joviality and quick humour, relieved me somewhat.

I soon settled down and there was no question of my parents enquiring about my whereabouts all this time, as they assumed I was at college studying for my A-levels.

The Maxwell children were staying in the house and they were very friendly towards me. Isabel and Anne compared their lives with mine and we talked at length in the sauna about our respective contacts with the opposite sex. From what I heard, R.M. was very strict with his daughters and made a point of finding out whom they were seeing.

Isabel told me a rather bizarre story. She said she had told her father she was going to the Maxwell bookshop. Incidentally, R.M. had very kindly told me I could go there whenever I wanted and said I could put any purchase on his account. Isabel said she had gone to the shop where she had met a man who had interested her. The man invited her downstairs where they had coffee and exchanged addresses. When she returned home, R.M. called her into his study.

'Was there something you wanted, Daddy?'

'Yes. Go over there and sit down.'

Isabel obeyed.

'You said you were going to the bookshop to have a look around. You met a man there, didn't you?'

'Only by chance, Daddy.'

R.M. looked at his teenage daughter sternly.

'I'm disappointed in you, Isabel. You have deceived your father.'

'That's a strange story,' I said. I climbed down from the wooden benches to ladle more water on to the coals and poured more water over myself.

'Surely you couldn't have taken the incident too seriously,' I said.

'Perhaps your father was over-reacting. Maybe he didn't quite understand what happened.'

'I felt dreadful about it for several months.'

'Several months? You get over a trivial incident like that in twenty-four hours or forty-eight at the most.'

Isabel seemed annoyed.

'You don't understand, I felt my father couldn't trust me.'

'Nobody in the world trusts me but I don't get into a state for several months about it.'

'Was your father very strict with you?' she asked.

'Yes. He was kind but stern, particularly if he was disobeyed. When I was about eight, he said: "Don't ever go down to the swimming-pool alone." I had just learnt to swim and I wondered why I wasn't to go there alone. I assumed there was something there that he didn't want me to see so I went there straight away, when I thought he wasn't looking. Without my knowledge, he was doing some gardening nearby and he saw me coming back. I had a spanking but I deserved it.'

'If my father had told me not to do a thing, I would never have dreamt of doing it,' said Isabel. 'You sound as if you were very naughty. What else did you do?'

'I poured a bucket of gravel into my father's driver's bowl of clean oil. My parents made me learn *The Charge of the Light Brigade* as a punishment. My mother even suggested I should go to the driver's house and recite it to him on his doorstep. My father said this wouldn't be fair on him because of my monotonous voice!'

Isabel and Anne laughed.

'Would you like me to recite it now?'

'I'd much rather you didn't,' said Isabel.

Isabel appeared to be the most serious of her siblings. Her identical twin sister, Christine, took life more lightly. When I saw the photograph of R.M.'s original family, I was struck by her resemblance to R.M.'s mother, Hannah Hoch. Both their faces had a similar saintly serenity. Isabel had a good sense of humour but a quiet, reserved temperament. She was always gentle and kindly whenever I saw her.

She said: 'I'm afraid I've got to go now. I've got to get on with my essay. I'm due to read it to my tutor in the morning.'

I spoke to Anne.

'So what are you doing in life?'

This time it was her turn to ladle more water on to the coals.

'I'm going to be an actress. That is after I've got my degree. My father said I couldn't study drama before finishing at University.'

'Your father strikes me as being quite strict with you all. Do you get on with him?'

Anne, who was shy, was taken aback by my question. I was sorry I asked it. She moved up to the top tier, saying how hot she was.

'I love my father and I'm proud of him and all the wonderful things he did during the war. It's true he's strict and can be unreasonable, but he loves us all and bullies us into working like skivvies so that we can excel in life. Whenever I have a problem, provided of course it's not a woman's problem, he's strong and supportive. The only person he's dotingly indulgent towards, and spoils, is Ghislaine.'

'Ghislaine? I haven't met her yet.'

Anne came down again and watered the coals.

'Ghislaine's staying with a school friend. I don't know whether you know this but my brother, Michael, was in a coma for some years following a road accident. I remember the date when his life support machine was turned off. It was 27th January 1968. It was in the Churchill Hospital that he died. We were very close. Ghislaine was born three days after Michael's accident. It was several years before his life support machine was turned off.'

'I'm so sorry. It must have been awful for you.'

'It was. He was coming back from a party. He was a passenger in a car which collided with a stationary truck. As soon as Ghislaine was born, we all thought she was a gift from Heaven. My father spoils her like I said. She gets away with more than we ever did. She's nine now – nine and naughty.'

Not long after I had settled in the house, I was fed up with my hair colour. I decided to dye it black like R.M.'s and I wore it in a long plait, braided with ribbon to match whatever I wore. I was unaware of the fact that I looked like a middle-aged Chinaman.

I was afraid of dyeing it in the house in case I made a mess, so I walked up the drive to the offices of Pergamon Press and dyed it in one of the washrooms there.

R.M. was in his sombre study adjacent to his Empire drawing room, looking at papers. I went over to him to kiss him as I always did the first time I saw him each day. He got up and kissed me on the mouth.

31

'My God, Ellie, why the hell have you done this to your hair?'

'I got fed up with the old colour. I needed a change. Besides, women are always dying their hair.'

'But black doesn't suit you or your colouring. Your natural hair was so lovely and you can't change nature.'

'Sorry, Bob,' I said. 'I'll wait till it grows out. I can't reverse it now.'

Ghislaine, the youngest, came into the room, wearing blue jeans, tennis shoes and a white T-shirt. She clambered on to her father's knee and put her arms round his neck. He smothered her with loud smacking kisses.

'Who's that with you, Daddy?'

'That's not how one talks,' said R.M. 'One says: "My name's Ghislaine. I don't think I've met you before".'

Ghislaine repeated his words.

'I'm Eleanor. I'm a friend of your family. Nice to meet you.'

We shook hands.

'Why's your hair the same colour as Daddy's?'

'Don't be cheeky, Ghislaine,' said R.M.

Ghislaine had been given a horse by her father. It was a time in her life when she loved horses before discovering men. The gate of the tennis court had been left open and her horse had wandered on to the court, leaving mounds of dung everywhere. It had also eaten its way through the net.

I was walking round the garden with R.M. We came to the tennis court. Ghislaine was lying on her back on the ground outside with her legs crossed, playing 'God Save the Queen' on a recorder.

'What's your horse doing on the tennis court?' R.M. asked mildly.

'I can't help it if some idiot leaves the gate open.'

R.M. turned from subdued anger to merriment, caused by my hysterical giggles.

'It's not that I mind so much about your horse being on the tennis court,' he said, 'but what I can't tolerate is its leaving its visiting card.'

I stayed talking to Ghislaine for some time. Though cheeky, there was a natural sweetness about her. She told me she was due to get a prearranged hiding from R.M. that afternoon.

'What did you do to irritate him?'

'Oh, I asked Judy and Jean to do a complicated job for me,

32

without asking him.'

'Who are Judy and Jean and what did you ask them to do?'

'I told them to organize the transport of some horses – mine, and some friends' horses, too. I told Judy and Jean – Judy Ennals and Jean Baddeley, two of Daddy's secretaries – to make arrangements for the horses to be taken to Basingstoke for a point-to-point, and returned to Oxford afterwards.'

'Did these secretaries say they would carry out your orders?'

'Oh yes. I told them my father had said it was all right.'

'Did he say it was all right?'

'No, of course not. You must be joking.'

I lit a cigarette in amazement. She asked me if she could have one too but I said no.

'You're very naughty. How old are you?'

'Nine.'

'When you said your father was going to give you a "hiding" this afternoon, what sort of a hiding will it be?'

She looked nonplussed as if she thought she didn't deserve to be punished.

'Daddy has a series of things lined up in a row. There's a riding crop with a swish to it, another straight riding crop and a few shoehorns. He always asks me to choose which one I want.'

'Which one will you choose?' I asked.

'The shoehorn. That's the easiest.'

'What, for him or for you?'

'For me of course. If you were in my place, which one would you choose?'

By now, we were standing in a room next to the Boardroom and I saw the various instruments of discipline in a row. I became peculiarly excited but hid this from her.

'I'd choose this one,' I said light-heartedly. 'The one with the swishing movement.'

I waved it through the air and it made a whirring noise as I went through the motions of striking an invisible object.

'Why would you choose that? It's the worst.'

I suddenly remembered I was talking to a child. I wondered what would happen if she told her father I had been discussing this sort of thing with her. She looked up at me, baffled.

'Why would you choose the one that hurts the most? I don't understand.'

I got nervous.

'Because from what you told me, you've been very naughty. A nine-year-old can't give orders to busy secretaries about horses. You should know better at your age, judging by all the trouble you've caused, and your punishment should fit the crime. Had I behaved like that at your age, I would have been locked in my room and made to learn passages from Shakespeare by heart!'

Ghislaine seemed angry with me for not sympathizing with her.

'Would *you* like to be beaten by my father?' she shouted suddenly.

The words 'Oh, Christ, yes!' were struggling to be released by my tongue. I controlled myself.

'I – I – I – er.'

'Answer my question!' (She sounded like her father.)

'I don't give orders about horses to other people's secretaries. Nor do I respond to barked questions from nine-year-olds!' I said in mock anger. 'Does your father ride?'

'Not now he doesn't, but when he went fearlessly into battle, before getting his MC, flashing his sword in the shining sun, I feel sure he rode a horse!'

I suddenly felt very moved and endeared towards this pretty little girl with her pony tail and her father's black eyes. I was surprised by her advanced vocabulary. I was terrified that she would steer the conversation back to the embarrassing subject I had no wish to discuss.

'When I went up the drive to your father's offices, I saw some puppies with one of the secretaries. They're so sweet,' I said guardedly.

She became animated.

'Yes. They're the puppies Tiger had. She and Whisky, our two Labradors, had them together. Daddy often gives puppies to his secretaries. Some of the puppies are still in the basket with Mummy.'

'Where is the basket?'

'In the kitchen. Mummy's there now with Oping, preparing lunch.'

'Who's Oping?'

'Don't you know who Oping is? She's one of the Filipino ladies who help in the house.'

I went to the kitchen where I found Betty and Oping peeling

34

potatoes. I greeted Betty and introduced myself to Oping who had a cheerful, smiling face.

'What have you been doing all the morning, Elénore?'

'I've been in the sauna with Isabel and Anne. I went for a walk with Bob and I've been talking to Ghislaine.'

'Ghislaine?' said Betty. 'She's in disgrace with Bob and me. Her behaviour has been quite appalling.'

'Indeed? I heard from someone in the house that there had been some trouble in relation to horses,' I said vaguely.

'I don't want to talk about that. Come and keep me company.'

I helped her with the potato-peeling while she talked to me of love, literature, philosophy and life. What a magnificent mind she showed, what supreme sensitivity to art, music and beauty, and what a phenomenal and touching vision of the importance of human kindness. We spoke of Maupassant, Flaubert, Dostoievsky and Proust, among countless other literary figures.

She knew the volumes of *À la recherche du temps perdu* intimately. Later at University, I had to study its many volumes, but confess with shame that I only read a synopsis of it in English just before my Finals.

'The most wonderful thing about Proust,' she said, 'is his preoccupation with the details the human mind sometimes misses. So many people take art and fortune for granted. Those with too much money, unable to put it to intelligent use, become idle and self-pitying. There are stockbrokers' wives forever sobbing into their gin and tonics, because they don't set themselves constructive occupational projects.'

I had to laugh when she said this. I tried to imagine what a gin and tonic would taste like laced with a discontented housewife's tears. I wondered if it would still be drinkable.

She peeled the last of the potatoes and Oping took them from her and put them in a saucepan of boiling water. She continued.

'Do you think that an empty-headed stockbroker's wife or a débutante would notice the things Proust noticed? I remember feeling very sad one day when the City were getting at Bob. I read one of Proust's tomes and found an intricate description of someone's balcony. Every inch of the fretwork was described in microscopic detail, even the shape of the beaks of the tiny bronze birds intertwined with the railings.

'I felt that if a human eye could be capable of remembering an object of beauty, just through walking past it, there would be no sadness in the world, except in the hearts of the impoverished or the bereaved. Do you know Keats's poem which begins "No, No! go not to Lethe"?'

'I know the one you mean. I had to write an essay on it but I confess I don't know it by heart. In comparison with you I'm a Philistine. When I feel sad, I don't go out and gape at the country-side, which doesn't do much for me anyway as I prefer to be surrounded by concrete buildings. I'm a *Lethe* person. I go out and get pissed. That usually does the trick.'

She laughed. I was relieved not to have shocked her.

'You really are a one! That's what Bob likes about you so much.'

I loved Betty and I still do. In fact, since R.M.'s tragic death, about which I will speak later, I would be prepared to do anything in the world for her, because she is the very epitome of perfection. She even got up early to drive me to the examination hall, to help me to be more relaxed when I was doing my A-levels in English, French and Russian, before going to University. She would wait outside the hall and take me out to lunch to put me at my ease before sitting my next examination. No one else in the world would have done a thing like that.

'Ghislaine told me you had some puppies in here,' I said. 'May I see them?'

'Why, yes. They're over there.'

Six puppies, small enough to sleep in a man's shoe, played on a rug, surrounded by wire netting. Betty very kindly offered me one but I had to refuse it, because my lifestyle was unsuitable. As we went back to the other part of the kitchen, I noticed a padlock on the larder door.

'What goes on behind that door?' I asked.

'It's the larder. We have to lock it to keep Bob out when we put him on a diet; otherwise, he goes in and eats everything there is. He broke in only the other day, as he's so strong he can break any door down. We had to change the lock. He's so naughty sometimes. Let's go next door and have a drink.'

The seven children were in the living room. R.M., who had been working all morning in the Pergamon offices, was standing behind the bar like a publican. He was in a good mood.

'What will you have, Missy?'

'White wine, please.'

'You'll be getting white wine at lunch. Have something stronger.'

'I'd like a gin and tonic, then.'

'Gin and tonic, it shall be.'

He gave me the glass and I took a few gulps. I had a sense of euphoria as I stood there looking at R.M., feeling the warmth of the gin as it reached my stomach.

He came away from the bar and gave his familiar wolf-whistle.

'Come on everybody, let's go and have lunch.'

The children rose from their chairs immediately, as if responding to a military command. Everybody took their seats at the table in the dining room overlooking the lawn. I sat on R.M.'s right. Jean Baddeley, his personal assistant, chief henchman and the only person in the world apart from his tyrannical father, who was allowed to give him orders, sat on his left.

Food was passed round the table by one of the affable Filipinos. I was hungry so I took more potatoes than I thought I needed. The dishes were passed to R.M. who took an even larger amount of them.

Jean Baddeley, his personal assistant, turned furiously to the Filipino lady.

'I gave you specific instructions that Mr Maxwell was not to be offered potatoes!'

She took the spoon from the servant and shovelled the massive amount of potatoes off the wretched man's plate. To my surprise, he said absolutely nothing and I suddenly felt intensely jealous of the power Jean Baddeley appeared to wield over him.

I picked up my own potatoes with my pudding spoon and put them on his plate.

'I wouldn't stand for that, Bob,' I said. 'Anyway, you're not fat so there's no need for you to be on a diet.'

He turned to face me and I noticed a look of love in his eyes.

'Oh, you are sweet!' he said.

After lunch Isabel, the serious one, took me aside.

'Please don't do that again,' she said (very tactfully). 'Dad has a problem in relation to food and we all have to struggle to stop him harming himself.'

'What do you mean – harming himself? Why would potatoes harm someone?'

She lowered her voice as if about to break tragic news. I was getting increasingly confused.

'Once he starts eating carbohydrates, he can't stop. Why else do you think we are locking him out of the larder at night? Do you know that he's only got one lung?'

'Yes.'

'The lung has to do the work of two. Extra strain is put on his heart with all this eating. Jean and I have to work really hard to keep him healthy, and today you undid precisely what we're trying to do.'

I couldn't understand what was going on. It was as if she were talking about a very elderly, ailing dog, not a 46-year-old hot-blooded, Samson-like Cossack.

At that time. R.M. was well covered in an attractive sort of way, but not particularly fat. I decided the whole curious affair was none of my business.

'Sorry, Isabel, I won't do it again,' I said.

I stayed in the house for a few weeks. I was having breakfast with the family in the kitchen one day when the phone rang and R.M. answered it. My mother was on the line and asked to speak to me. She asked why I had been away for so long. She said in short that I had been with the Maxwells for longer than the ethics of hospitality permitted, and told me to come home. I went back to the table and sat down with Bob who had locked himself into his eating.

'Pamela [my mother] wants you back, blast it!' he said irritably.

I kept in touch with the family and saw them again within a few weeks, when R.M. asked me to come and work for him in his Buckinghamshire constituency during the 1970 election campaign.

He and his family occupied a small, pleasant house, overlooking a stagnant canal. Jean Baddeley, who knew I was coming, organized a rigidly strict bath rota and had a long talk with me about the exact time I was to take a bath, as well as its duration which was not to exceed ten minutes.

These events coincided with an anti-airport rally in a town in Buckinghamshire, organized by a once Tory barrister, Desmond Fennell. The Berrys had invited R.M., Fennel and his wife, Susan, to lunch before attending the rally and R.M. gave me a lift. My siblings, Nicky and Harriet, were there but my other brother was covering a story in America. All I remember about this lunch is that R.M. had been put on yet another diet by Jean Baddeley and Isabel, who had lectured him about the importance of keeping to his diet. He refused to eat anything except soup.

Lunch was hurried and, afterwards, a number of cars set out from the house and steamed towards the rally. Mr Hoppitt, R.M.'s driver, said he knew the way. R.M. stayed a while after the others had gone, because he liked flowers and wanted me to show him the garden. There's nothing that bores me more than showing people round gardens, about which I know nothing, but it was nice to see the delight R.M. showed when looking at the flowers. He reminded me of Ferdinand the Bull.

'What are you doing with your life, Eleanore?' he asked suddenly.

'Studying languages.'

'Which ones?'

'French,' I said. My father was paying for me to do an extensive French course. I wanted to learn Russian but my parents said I couldn't until I'd mastered French. Hence, I spent hours each day teaching myself Russian from tapes and grammar books and, because my will to learn it was so great, I had secretly become fluent in six months. I wasn't quite sure whether I should tell R.M. my secret.

He had a conversation with me in French. He appeared satisfied by the way I spoke it.

'Do you mean to tell me you only speak one language besides English?'

'No, I speak Russian too.' He seemed peculiarly impressed. We had a conversation in Russian, in which I expressed thoughts and told stories I would never have dared tell in English.

While this was going on, my father was looking for us. All the cars had left with the exception of my father's and R.M.'s Rolls-Royce, occupied by Hoppitt, the chauffeur.

'Come on, Bob, it's time to go,' said my father.

'Hullo, Michael. God, you've got a smasher of a daughter!'

'Oh indeed? Don't say that in front of her. It will go to her head. Whose car are you going in?' he asked me.

'I'm going with Bob,' I said.

We spoke Russian for the whole journey. Hoppitt lost my father's car and neither of us knew how to get to the town where the rally was being held. It was evident that R.M. did not have the same interest in the airport as the others. He told Mr Hoppitt to stop outside a pub where we got out for a drink.

We arrived at the rally half an hour late because Hoppitt had been holding his map upside down. R.M. hit him on the head with a rolled up copy of the *Guardian*.

Apparently, as the rally had been going on for 15 minutes, my parents were asking agitatedly where R.M. and I were. Nicky thought the whole situation amusing and Harriet raised her eyebrows in mischievous curiosity.

To get to the front row where my family were sitting, you had to walk down the aisle of a church-like building. Fennell, at the helm, stopped the speeches to wait for R.M.

He and I arrived. I was intoxicated by this time so I had to hold on to his arm. We sat on either side of my father and mother in the front row. We spoke Russian across my astounded father, regardless of the silence throughout the hall.

By this time my mother turned to us, thinking we were making the words up.

'Aren't you impressed by the way Eleanore's taught herself Russian, without any help at all?' said R.M.

'I think it's absolutely extraordinary,' said my mother. 'She's very clever to have done all that herself. You haven't been teaching her, have you?'

'No. It's obviously a gift.'

My father leant across R.M. who was sitting with one leg crossed over the other at right angles.

'Why do you speak fluent Russian when we sent you out to perfect your French? Come clean, out with it!'

Fennell banged the table for silence. He meant business and he didn't want the hall to be filled with the sound of Robert Maxwell and me speaking Russian.

R.M. promised to send me the complete Pergamon Russian course. He kept his promise and two weeks later a crate, its contents worth over £300, arrived on the doorstep. It contained tapes and reproduced sections of Tolstoy, as well as other Russian authors. Accompanied by this present, was a sweet letter from R.M.

*   *   *

Once in the Wharf House, when I was working for him, Jean put us all on her notorious bath rota system. She had obviously remembered my habits, following my long stay with the family. Because of the severity of my illness, I had taken baths up to seven or eight times a day, laced with Dettol and pine essence, and scoured my skin with a scrubbing brush saturated in Vim, in a pathetic attempt to wash the disease away. After this process, I would empty the bath and fill it up with the same ingredients and start again, repeating the procedure three times.

Although there were a number of bathrooms at Headington Hill Hall, the one allocated to me was at the top of the house and I shared it with the luckless Jean Baddeley, who complained that there was never any hot water for her, and that the bathroom stank of disinfectant and Vim, as well as being permanently occupied.

In the Wharf House, there was only one bathroom.

'Mr Maxwell takes his bath at 5.00 a.m.,' said Jean. 'Woe betide you if you're in there then.'

'OK, Jean, I won't be awake anyway at that hour.'

It was 3.00 o'clock one morning. I woke up with an agonizingly obsessive urge to take another bath. I assumed no one would be awake at that hour. Not so. R.M. banged peremptorily on the door at 3.30, while I lay, reading Edgar Allan Poe, in a piping bath on the other side of it.

'Philip! [his son], what the fucking hell are you doing in there?' he shouted.

'It's not Philip. It's Eleanor,' I said. As I spoke, I upset a bottle of Dettol onto *The Raven*. R.M. sounded pissed off.

'All right, I suppose I'll be able to come back in another three hours!' he said in the tone of an out-of-work funeral director.

The rota didn't seem to work, despite Jean's arduous organizing efforts. I went in one morning at 9.00 and got up to my usual habits which had not died although the disease had.

'Elénore! What are you doing? Can you buck up?'

Betty needed to get in at the same time, because the times of the rota had overlapped. This presented an ongoing problem. I arranged to take baths in the council house of a factory foreman called Dave who was also working for R.M. At that time, I was still dyeing my hair black, which I did every two days, and I inadvertently blackened the foreman's towels. I didn't know what to do about this, whether to confess to the foreman and buy him a new set of towels, or to say nothing. I decided to say nothing.

I tried another house belonging to a Maxwell worker, but my reputation had radiated through the entire North Bucks Labour

41

Party, so the gentleman told me very politely to take my baths elsewhere.

I found out that in Milton Keynes there was a public swimming pool to visit whenever I needed to immerse myself in water. A singularly unattractive man kept following me about. He followed me into one of the changing rooms and said, 'If you strip, I can give you a nice towelling down.'

'I don't want a nice towelling down or a nasty towelling down,' I said, 'I am certainly not prepared to engage myself in a sexual incident in Mr Maxwell's constituency, unless with Mr Maxwell, himself.'

I did not go there again.

4

I still had trouble getting up in the mornings. There was no clock-in time at the Party Headquarters so I wandered in whenever I felt like it. One of my duties was to wind the handle of a printing press producing photographs of R.M. – this was by far my favourite job. I also had to sit in a row with a lot of jolly, ribald old ladies, passing documents down the line, stamping them, folding them up and putting them in envelopes.

I was happy in their company and in my surroundings. As we worked we cracked filthy jokes. R.M. came in and overheard us one day. He pushed our chairs, with us still sitting on them, to separate tables scattered over the large hall, muttering something about lewd talk giving the Labour Party a bad name. Then he did the same to the chairs occupied by about ten other workers, and pushed them, with the workers still sitting on them, to the table he'd taken us away from.

All this took him about five minutes. As he moved me over he said, 'You'll be pleased to hear I'm putting you next to a very good-looking man, so be sure to keep your conversation nice and clean.'

'Forgive me, Bob,' I said sweetly, looking him straight in the eye with a seductive smile. He returned the smile.

'I'll forgive you but will the Almighty forgive you?'

The man I was put next to was a saucy fellow called Chris Smith. His conversation was even coarser than that of the old ladies. He had an anal sense of humour and when R.M. went back to his office, he talked about the various disciplinary departments in the sex shops he had visited.

'Chris, Bob said no lewd talk,' I said.

'It's all right now. He's in his office.'

I liked Chris Smith. We often went drinking together. He was chatty and vivacious, but occasionally moody. He was neither cultured nor book-read but he nearly always had a joke to tell, accompanied by an infectious laugh.

Sometimes, he took off my voice. I couldn't make up my mind about this. Part of me thought how funny it was. The other part was irritated.

* * *

The Labour Party canvassing van was an impressive sight, covered with such slogans as *Harold and Bob will finish the job.* Mr Hoppitt was behind the wheel and R.M. would stand up with his head and shoulders protruding through the roof talking through a megaphone.

'Vote when you can. Maxwell's yer man,' he would boom with hypnotic, if monotonous repetition. 'Stop the van, Mr Hoppitt,' he said suddenly.

Hoppitt swerved in towards the pavement, on which a middle-aged woman was walking with her dog.

'Morning, madam,' said R.M. in a friendly tone. 'That charming Basset of yours – what's his name?'

The woman turned round, looking inappropriately hostile.

'It's not a Basset, it's a Border Terrier, and if you really want to know, it's name's Jeff.'

R.M. looked piqued. 'Come on, Mr Hoppitt, let's go,' he said.

Canvassing always took place in the evenings. I was prepared to do plenty of clerical work in the afternoons so I saw no point in getting up early.

In the Headquarters, I met another, older man, also working for R.M. He was the Branch Secretary of a union and his name was Arthur Leary. He had a pleasant, gentle face, framed by thick snow-white hair and he was devoted to R.M.

When I wasn't doing my favourite job, turning the handle of the printing press which, as well as R.M.'s photograph, churned out pamphlets called Maxwellgrams, I worked at a table with Chris Smith and Arthur Leary. We had to put stacks of envelopes into rubber bands and throw them into baskets.

If I wasn't having lunch at the Wharf House, Chris, Arthur, Jean and I went out to a restaurant. I had a voracious appetite for food at that time, and was never satisfied with what I ordered. I drank quite a lot which made me hungrier still, and I leant over the table with my fork, taking things from Chris's, Arthur's and Jean's plates.

44

Arthur was half amused and half irritated. He took me into R.M.'s office after lunch and spoke to him in a heavy Yorkshire brogue.

'Your little girlfriend tairks things from oother people's plairts!'

R.M. looked disinterested.

'Don't worry about that, Arthur. I've taught her to take what she wants out of life,' he said.

I went canvassing that afternoon, accompanied by Betty and Molly, one of the old ladies who cracked coarse jokes. Molly was forthright and unusually talkative, like a washerwoman. Each time a bemused housewife answered the door, Molly launched into a manic monologue, expressing R.M.'s virtues to her.

I heard the shrill French voice of Betty who was sitting in the car.

'Molly! Come back to the car and get in!'

'Molly's not to canvass for me any more,' said R.M. across the table to Betty at dinner.

'Who told you about Molly's canvassing?'

'Oh, just other canvassers.'

Up to now, I had been going from house to house with Betty.

'I want Eleanore to go out alone,' said R.M. 'I think it would give her a lot of self-confidence and gain me a lot of votes.'

I felt very proud out there on my own with my pile of leaflets and the pictures of R.M. that I had printed on the machine myself.

I started on a line of red brick houses with neatly kept gardens.

'I'm canvassing on behalf of Robert Maxwell, the Labour candidate. Can we be counting on your support on Polling Day?'

The woman I faced was in her late sixties and wearing a neat brown dress. She came to the door knitting, and went on knitting as I spoke to her.

'Sorry, dear,' she said with a smile, 'I'm a rabid Conservative.'

I got roughly the same reaction from the people behind the next few doors. I was getting bored and I thought of ticking off everyone on the list as being Tory, but I knew R.M. wouldn't like that so I didn't.

The tenth house along was shabbier than the others and the garden was overgrown. I knocked on the door. A man came to the door, in shirt sleeves, looking like a gangster from Sapper.

'Fuck off, you common red tart!'

45

It was then that I made a monstrous mistake, one which I am embarrassed about to this day. I turned on my heels.

'Bob! A nasty man's just called me a red tart,' I told R.M. later.

He looked up from his papers and stared at me with his head lowered and his eyes raised, showing the whites. He often effected this pose when something either hurt or displeased him.

'Well, what did our Eleanore do about that?' he asked, his expression quizzical.

'I ran away,' I said, without thinking.

He banged his hand (his left hand) down on the desk.

'I won't have to do with people who walk away like frightened dogs with their tails between their legs! We Maxwells don't do that sort of thing. We Maxwells are tough. I thought I'd tutored you well. Next time, you hit back. Do you understand?'

'Yes, Bob.'

I went out and got systematically drunk.

A few days later, I had an opportunity to please R.M. by doing what he wanted. I had to canvass a street in a much rougher area. Most of its inhabitants told me they would be voting Labour. I came to a door, opened by a thin but muscular man with sandy-coloured hair and a torn white boiler suit. I could see a lot of rubbish in his hall and the banister on the facing staircase was about to fall off.

The man strode out of his house.

'So you're Labour, are you? It's because of this fucking Labour government that I've been out of work for five years! If you don't piss off, I'll give you a good backhander.'

'Hit me then, you bastard, see if I care!' I said.

'You ain't fucking worth it.'

He turned round and went indoors.

Jean was canvassing the same street and had heard some of the dialogue between us. She looked impressed.

'My God, I've never seen anything like it!' she said. 'I wouldn't have dared do that.' I was hoping she would report the incident to R.M., which I thought would impress him more than my telling him myself.

She drove me back to the Wharf House. We both went into R.M.'s study for a drink.

'You should have seen Eleanor just now. I thought that man was going to kill her.'

'Come on, Basso Profundo, what happened? Let's have it.'

I told him a few lies and gained some strange excitement from doing so. I told him that the man had asked me if I wanted him to give me a 'good shag' and that I had told him I doubted he'd ever be able to 'get it up'.

R.M. roared with laughter. When he stopped laughing, he asked me a really bizarre question, still smiling.

'Were you very depressed afterwards?'

'Depressed?'

'Depressed.'

'No. Why should I be? I know I slipped up the other day but I like a socking good confrontation. It's like a gin and tonic.'

He gave me a very serious look and leant forwards in his chair.

'To do what you did then required a hell of a lot of courage. Do you know that?'

'Yes perhaps.' (I felt as a heroin addict feels after his first fix.)

The next few days, I was happy. I worked hard, enjoying the company of my fellow workers and canvassing every evening.

Chris Smith and I were canvassing on opposite sides of a street in Newport Pagnell, a sedate, xenophobic country village. I walked up a tall, steep flight of steps, my hands full of leaflets and photographs of R.M. and knocked on the door. The woman I saw before me appeared in her late sixties and was thin with a hollow face and hostile, beady eyes.

'I'm canvassing on behalf of Robert Maxwell, the Labour candidate. Can we be counting on your vote next Thursday?'

The woman stared at me. I stared back at her until she averted her gaze. Suddenly, she formed her wizened hands into fists and for some unknown reason, started to pummel me with increasing ferocity.

'Get yourself and your stinking literature off my threshold!' Her accent wasn't local. She could have been a colonial. She seized my pictures of R.M. and screwed them into a ball which she threw into the street.

I waited to see what she was going to do next and I didn't wait in vain. She continued to pummel me with her left hand and extended her right arm in a Nazi salute.

The woman sang the National Anthem. I waited for her to finish and only just managed to keep a straight face.

'You're bloody bonkers,' I said. 'Do you know that?'

47

The next thing I knew was that the maniac had pushed me down her steps. I was still holding the canvassing sheet. I took out my pen, and with a trembling hand wrote against the woman's name. 'VERY DANGEROUS WOMAN!'

Chris Smith came over to me and helped me up. He looked at the canvassing sheet and my words beside the woman's name. He let out a guffaw. My arm was hurting so Chris drove me back to the Wharf House.

R.M. was in the kitchen, cooking scrambled eggs. He wasn't wearing a jacket and his tie was loosened at the neck with the top buttons of his shirt undone. His appearance drove me crazy.

Chris had already told Jean what had happened.

'She was attacked, Mr Maxwell,' she said.

'Attacked? Christ!' shouted R.M. 'Sit down and I'll bring you some scrambled eggs I've cooked.'

He brought two plates of scrambled eggs over to the table and sat down. I told him the story while he listened, fascinated. The scrambled eggs were cooked in butter and were good. It surprised me that he knew how to cook. I later learnt that he often cooked when he was alone and that cooking was one of his hobbies.

He was giving me a wonderful audience which made me forget the pain in my arm.

'So you say the batty old woman started hitting you?'

'Yes, that's right. This is what she did.'

I did the same to R.M. as she had done to me. I hit his arms and I realized how cuddly he was. He threw back his head and laughed, looking me straight in the eye.

'Steady, Missy, you're beating me up!'

I did a demonstration of the woman singing the National Anthem as she saluted with one hand and went on hitting me with the other. I couldn't get the co-ordination right. My right hand mimicking the Nazi salute, kept hitting R.M., while my left hand didn't know whether to give the salute or do the hitting.

'You hurt your arm when she pushed you, didn't you, Missy?'

'Yes,' I said.

R.M. put two fingers of each hand into his mouth and whistled. Jean came in. 'I do wish you'd stop that whistling, Mr Maxwell, every time you need attention. It's dreadfully common.'

'It's what they do at football grounds, isn't it?'

'What do you want, Mr Maxwell?'

'Get a doctor, please. I think she may have broken her arm.'

'It's OK. I don't need a doctor,' I said.

I went canvassing with my arm in a sling with Chris Smith again the next evening, in an equally xenophobic country village. I knocked on a door which was opened by an unshaven drunk. The man supported himself on the open door of his house, and looked at me through watery red eyes, exhaling the smell of stale beer.

'I don't vote for crooks!' he said.

'Your words constitute slander in the first degree and they will be written down. Written down, I tell you.'

The man tried to slam the door in my face but I rammed my foot in.

'What you really resent about this man is that he started with less than you and got further. You're a petty-minded, provincial oaf,' I shouted.

The man swayed backwards and forwards as if about to fall. I heard Chris's voice behind me.

'Leave him, now. Just mark "no" on the canvass sheet and move on. Don't get into any arguments.'

Two days later, R.M. called me into his office.

'What is it, Bob?'

He was looking as serious as a High Court Judge. I was terrified he was going to notify me of an illness or a bereavement.

'What's happened, Bob?'

He came to the point without preamble.

'Eleanore! You are NOT to frighten my constituents.'

'I haven't frightened anyone! What are you talking about? Whom have I frightened?'

R.M. cleared his throat, sounding like a gang of Hell's Angels trying to start their motor bikes.

'We all know about this,' he said. 'There's something about the way you approach people that terrifies them. Even I find you a bit scary at times.'

'But it was you who taught me to do that. That's why I do it, and I don't even know I'm doing it.'

'Yes, I understand that. Frighten anyone you want, but not in my bloody constituency. I'm trying to win this election for Christ's sake!'

'All right, Bob. I won't do it again, I promise.'

'It's all right. I know your heart's in the right place but as of tomorrow, I'll have to get Philip to go round with you.'

Philip is one of Bob's sons. He is quiet, humorous and gentle. He has not inherited his father's looks and resembles his paternal grandfather.

As we got out of the car to cover a street, he said, 'Whatever you do, don't shout at anyone, Ellie. You may come across some ghastly old fart, but be sure to be as polite as you possibly can.'

'No problem, Philip. Your father gave me a talking to last night.'

'I can well imagine he did! He sometimes tends to be the pot that calls the kettle black, if you'll pardon the cliché, but I love the old bastard all the same.'

Betty and I sometimes canvassed together. We shared an interest in the works of the Marquis de Sade. One day we took a break and sat down on a seat in a village street and had coffee from a flask she had brought with her. A heated, but friendly, argument ensued between us about whether the 1787 edition of the Marquis de Sade's *Justine* had more or fewer merits than the 1797 edition. She said the 1787 edition was better because of its theme that virtue is always rewarded and vice punished in the end. I did not adhere to this view. I said that whatever virtue is committed, it achieves nothing, not even a reward or acknowledgement.

One of the workers came up to us, leaning out of the campaign van, reminding us that lunch was at 1.00 o'clock and that it was now 1.30.

'Are you both all right?' asked the worker.

'Yes, perfectly,' said Betty. 'We were arguing about a Frenchman.'

*　　*　　*

I was standing in an idyllic village square with Chris and Arthur among a crowd. The scenario could have belonged to the eighteenth century. Creepers hung in abundance from the walls of a pub, outside which I saw three brawny, cloth-capped rustics sitting with their backs to the crowd, their braces so tight they looked as if they were about to snap. They were swigging from big brimming beakers of Newcastle brown ale and stuffing themselves with fish and chips.

They ate and drank in a gross and bestial manner, so engrossed in pumping rubbish into their stomachs that they didn't speak to each other although they appeared to know each other.

Looking at them, I formed an immediate opinion that they weren't very nice.

R.M.'s campaign van, driven by the phlegmatic Mr Hoppitt, pulled up in front of the crowd. The date was 10th June and R.M.'s supporters sang 'Happy Birthday' which appeared to irritate and embarrass him. He leant out of the roof of the van and addressed his audience, speaking as usual about pay rises, corrupt landlords persecuting the working classes, schools, tied cottages and that sort of thing.

I noticed the three sinister-looking rustics by now full of beer, staggering towards the crowd. Instinctively, I picked up a stick and moved through the crowd in their direction. I could tell they were up to no good.

One of them, a white-haired fellow, interrupted the speech at a point where R.M. was making a joke, a very bad one, I admit, but a joke nevertheless.

'It's lucky there's a fish and chip shop next to the pub, isn't it?'

'You wouldn't be standing up there like that if you'd been able to buy the *News of the World*,' said the white-haired rustic.

'I don't think this is an occasion to be personal,' said R.M.

The man pursued his quarry. I moved towards him clutching the stick, my heart awash with hatred. Doing so gave me sexual pleasure.

'How can you call yourself a socialist if you have a Rolls Royce and trusts for your children in Liechtenstein?' asked the rustic.

R.M. lost his temper.

'Your words are slanderous and you are deliberately instigating a smear campaign against me!'

I raised the stick, holding it behind my head to hit the man. My action roused me even more. I was about to bring it down on him.

'Eleanore! Naughty!' shouted R.M. I was so startled that I took three paces backwards, and slowly opened my hand to release the stick.

The alarming news transpired during the campaign that R.M.'s agent, a left-winger called Tim Miles (name disguised), had a grudge against him. It was said that he failed to do the administrative work required of him and apparently hassled his pro-R.M. deputy. Mick Scrivener (name disguised).

Scrivener was devoted to R.M. but suffered from a mental

illness, exacerbated by Miles's alleged insensitivities. Scrivener tried to tell R.M. what he rightly or wrongly thought was going on and referred incoherently to his mental illness. His methods of expressing his thoughts were muddled, confused and incomprehensible. R.M. became very impatient. He had no idea what he was talking about and ignored him.

Miles was alone in the campaign van which he had allowed to run out of petrol in a quiet village street. The loudspeakers were turned on and Miles started swearing his head off. Four-letter words blasted round the Labour Party Headquarters' loudspeakers like confetti.

Arthur Leary took command of the situation and rushed over to the microphone, aware that Miles's obscene tirade was reverberating all over the constituency.

'Watch the language you're using! Over.'

'I'll use what fucking language I want. I'm out of fuel.'

'I'll tell the Boss,' said Arthur assertively.

'Tell anyone you sodding well like. You know what I think of that bastard!'

R.M. came in after all this had happened.

'Where the hell's Miles, Arthur?'

'His van's broken down in a village street. He's out of fuel.'

'Bloody fool! Where the hell's Mick Scrivener?'

'I'm afraid he's had to go to a psychiatrist.'

'Why?'

'Because he said Miles had driven him off his head.'

'Why didn't he come to me?'

'He did but you weren't able to understand a word he said.'

'In that case, I don't think the psychiatrist will either.'

Arthur smiled politely and hinted to R.M. what he thought Miles was up to.

'I'm not too confident we're going to win this fucking election, Arthur,' said R.M.

R.M. was doing his 'surgery' the next day. An agitated woman brought her daughter, a waif-like creature aged about fifteen into his office and told him she was pregnant. She asked him what she should do about it.

R.M. addressed his questions to the girl rather than her mother.

'Why don't you marry the child's father, settle down and make a go of it?'

'I couldn't do that,' said the girl.

'Why not?'

'Because I don't know who the father is.'

'Why don't you know who the father is?' asked R.M., getting bored and impatient.

'Well, it could be one of five. It could be Eric, John, Martin, Ned or Ken. It was a Saturday night and I had a gang bang.'

R.M. looked aghast.

'Blimey, madam, you really have put my king in check!' was all he could think of saying.

This legendary story travelled all over the constituency, at the speed of light. It was told, with increasing exaggeration in pubs, cafés, among cinema audiences and many other places. It also got into the local paper.

Molly, the noisiest woman in the workforce, was always accompanied by her elderly mother who also made a lot of noise but wasn't as noisy as her daughter. Molly's maternal grandfather was in the Headquarters every day. He looked about 110 and the only reason for his permanent presence was that there was nobody at home to look after him.

He occupied a chair in the middle of the room with his head thrown back, his eyes closed and his toothless mouth gaping open. People seeing him for the first time assumed automatically that he was dead and quite a few women screamed.

Sometimes, R.M. resurrected the situation by walking past this man, ruffling up his snow-white hair and patting him on the shoulder, muttering, 'How yer doing, Grandpa?'

Betty was terrified of the man.

'Do we have to have him in here, Bob? He gives me the creeps. "Is he dead?" I keep asking myself.'

'No, of course he isn't bloody dead! He's got nowhere else to go.'

'But Papa [she often called him that], he seems in perpetual rigor. It makes the place look like a mortuary.'

'I've told you he can stay so that's it.'

'Is there any reason why he can't sit in your office?'

'I don't want him in my bloody office!' bellowed R.M.

The workers were used to assuming the old man was more likely to be dead than alive and he got accepted as part of the furniture.

It was during R.M.'s passionate Eve of Polls speech, when cameras clicked and flashed around him, making me indescribably roused, that it became apparent, on account of a very unpleasant odour, that the old man had indeed died. In fact, he'd been dead for some time and even R.M., with his repeated hair ruffling and 'How yer doing, Grandpa?' had no knowledge that he was talking to a stiff.

A small amount of scuffling took place around the man. R.M.'s speech was over after tumultuous applause and supporters began to shuffle out. A neat-looking man mounted the platform and gave R.M. a note. He read it and looked surprised.

'I think one ought to generally send for a hearse,' he said, in the voice of a man asking for a short back and sides.

'The bloomin' 'earse should have been 'ere two frigging weeks ago!' shouted a supporter. (He was a bit the worse for wear.)

When the workers gathered at the Wharf House, and as women clucked in clattering manic voices, I could hold out no longer. The whole situation had turned into a macabre farce. I was absolutely convulsed with giggles. I had trouble standing up.

'What's the matter, Eleanore?' asked Betty.

'Nothing. Just stomach ache. I'll go outside in the fresh air.'

'Has she got a temperature, Betty?' R.M.'s voice boomed from the other side of the room.

'No. No, Papa,' adding very quietly, 'Just women's problems, I think.'

Horrendously embarrassed, I staggered outside and lay on my stomach by the canal, waiting for the giggling attack to subside.

Attention had turned from stiffs to polls. I came back and saw R.M. in the hall.

'Feeling better, Eleanore?'

'I feel fine.'

I gave him a kiss and said, 'Good luck, Bob.'

'I may need it. Most people round here think I'm a bloody Bolshevik.'

Polling Day dragged on exhaustively. I got on a train to London where I voted Tory in my own constituency, because I felt like it at the time. Even so, I desperately wanted R.M. to win in his constituency so I took another train back to Milton Keynes, picked up my brother's car at the station and drove Labour Party supporters to the polls.

My behaviour that day made me feel pretty odd. I suppose any unimaginative psychiatrist would have tried to incarcerate me on a schizophrenia rap. I felt sweaty and disorientated but I had a gin and tonic after the Polls had closed and felt better.

It was on the cards, due to the Mori polls, that Labour would win on a landslide. I went into R.M.'s study accompanied by the whole family, Chris, Jean, Arthur and one or two other campaign workers. R.M. sat with his feet on the desk, and the top two buttons of his shirt undone and his tie loosened, which drove me into a frenzy. My eyes were more often focused on him than on the television.

After about an hour, it transpired that Labour was losing. R.M. muttered the word 'Christ!' a few times. Most of his family looked downcast, particularly Betty, and a few of the women were in tears.

When R.M.'s friend George Brown lost his seat and posed before cameras looking downcast, his cheeks tear-stained, there was a deadly silence in the room and R.M., who incidentally always cried very easily when sad, looked close to tears on watching his friend's grief.

The hush in the room was interrupted by a disastrously tactless remark coming from Ian, one of R.M.'s sons, then aged about 13, to his sister, Isabel, who was sitting on the floor by his side. Ian is a delightful person but there may well have been some occasions in his younger life when he offered the putter to someone whose ball was still in the bunker.

'What do you think, Izzy?' he said, his commanding voice raised. 'When it comes to Dad's seat, he'll lose narrowly after a couple of recounts? Let's bet on it, Izzy.'

Ian is a forthright, golden-hearted fellow but, like his father, he has a fairly robust temper if provoked. 'Don't you *dare* talk to my Dad about necrophilia!' he once shouted angrily at me. The incident I am referring to appears in one of the Anecdotes at the end of this book.)

When we were watching the results, Isabel did not answer her brother and lowered her head. R.M. looked away from the screen and focused his piercing eyes on his son.

'I'd watch it if I were you or you'll be sorry. That means I'll give you a good hiding.'

This made me very excited. I stayed where I was, sitting on the floor. I forced myself to look at the television, and not R.M.

The craggy face of Reginald Bosanquet filled the screen. He never struck me as being a particularly good-looking man. Anne, the oldest survivor of the Maxwell children, who was then a professional actress, evidently fancied Bosanquet and tried to cheer the gloomy atmosphere in the room. She mimicked a cockney accent.

''Ullo, dearie! Fancy a roll in the 'ay darlin'? Don't squeeze the fruit unless yer wants to buy it!'

Her spontaneous effort to provide comic relief had a profoundly irritating effect on her father, either because he may have considered her outburst vulgar, or because he failed to see there is a funny side to all things grave, or both. He lost his temper.

'For Christ's sake, shut up! I can't hear a bloody thing when you're cracking stupid jokes. One more sound out of you and I'll take you upstairs and tan your backside, as big as you are!'

These threats of the infliction of corporal punishment by the hand of this hunky male sex siren, looking dishevelled and wearing a loosened tie, were more than I could handle. The lust they inspired in me caused me to hyperventilate. I had to go upstairs and immerse myself in a stone-cold bath for half an hour. I returned to the study, assuming my absence was unnoticed.

'Where the hell have you been, Eleanore?' boomed R.M., his tone half angry. 'Surely you couldn't have had yet another bath? Jean said you had two already today.'

'Oh, no, no, I didn't take one!' I said. I was afraid of him knowing that I was lying, as well as the possibility that he might have asked me why I had taken one, in which case I might have had to tell him the truth outright.

He raised his head, his face in repose which he always did when he knew he was being lied to, but because the incident was trivial, he let it ride.

We stayed up until 4 a.m. by which time we knew the Tories were going to win by a landslide. R.M. sat, supporting his face with his hands – it was possible he may have been hiding his tears. The count in his constituency would not be taking place until late that morning. We were all exhausted. The workers shuffled despondently out of the study. I stayed. I went over to R.M. I wanted to be alone in his presence.

I knew he saw me coming so I turned away from him. I stood still. He ran his fingers through my hair and wound it into a knot. I wondered what he was going to do next. He turned me round and kissed me on the mouth, like a lover. He did not do anything else, at that time.

'Thank you so much, Ellie.'

'For what? I've failed. We all have.'

'You've got nerves of steel and your heart's in the right place. You mean more to me than you know.'

'Oh, do I? I'm not worth as much as you. After all, you saved my life, didn't you?'

I loitered a bit and wondered what else he was going to say. He guided me into the corridor, where a few workers were standing around aimlessly, looking sad. Poor Betty was among them. I felt very sorry for her.

R.M. turned to me, his tone slightly formal. 'I'm afraid it's a pretty full house. You'll have to share a room with Mick Scrivener. Aren't you the lucky one! There's a bunk in there. There's no need to worry about him making sexual advances. He isn't exactly a ladies' man.

'Thanks a lot, Bob,' I said.

R.M. gave me a bear hug before we went to our respective beds. I found Mick Scrivener lying face down on the top bunk, sobbing his guts out. I can't handle it when men cry and I stood there staring at him. At length, I managed to drag out some well-meaning but ill-chosen words.

'Why do you have to take things so hard, Mick? There'll be another election in five years and another five years after that. Besides, you did your best.'

'It's not that. It's that man.'

'What man?'

'Tim Miles. He hates Bob.'

I was exhausted and didn't want to hear any more about the unsatisfactory relations between Tim Miles and Mick Scrivener.

'You shouldn't have let him get to you,' I said impatiently. 'If a man ruffles another man, the ruffled man should beat the culprit up, instead of crying about it.'

Scrivener didn't answer. I got into the lower bunk. Although I sympathized, I wasn't interested in his problems. My main concern was that I might talk in my sleep and reveal my terrible secret that I had gone to London to vote Tory. I stuffed my mouth with tissue paper to prevent any movement of my tongue and gagged myself with a scarf.

When Betty came in to wake me, she was baffled by my appearance. I muttered something about fear of talking in my sleep and upsetting Mick by shouting foul language, and she took it as a joke.

We all set off in a convoy of cars and vans, not unlike a funeral procession, to the Buckingham Town Hall where the count was taking place.

All R.M.'s supporters, including myself, flocked into the market place outside the Town Hall. The gathering was rowdy and some sections of the crowd were angry and vicious. I have always had a *tricoteuse* mentality and I get carried away on the wave of mass hysteria. I edged over to the angry section of the crowd.

A rough, attractive-looking, well-built man, whose name I have forgotten, flashed a jagged-toothed grin at me. He was kneeling on the ground, brandishing a red flag with an intricately-embroidered hammer and sickle on it.

'Come on, El, get on my shoulders and wave the flag!' said the man.

I took a strong liking to this appealing, vibrant man and got on his shoulders. He forced his way to the front of the crowd with me on top of him, waving the flag in circles round my head.

The man lowered me to the ground outside the Town Hall. From a flag pole at the top of the building, the Union Jack billowed in the fresh June wind.

'Go on, El,' said the man, 'there's a fire-escape at the side of the building. Shin up it, take the Union Jack down and put the red flag in its place.'

I am unfit because I hate taking exercise. The idea of 'shinning' up a metal ladder, carrying a red flag, was daunting but it was a challenge. I have always been influenced by the slogan, 'Never Say No to a Dare'.

I gripped the red flag between my teeth and began to mount the ladder, without looking down. A surge of mania went through me. I recited the first few verses of *Horatius* to myself and finally dragged myself on to the roof.

I made my way towards the Union Jack. I lifted it from its berth and threw it over the edge of the building, just missing the crowd who descended on it like vultures and ripped it to pieces, cheering.

'Put up the flag, comrade! Put up the flag!' chanted the crowd in unison. I enjoyed showing off, and waves of euphoria went through me.

I did as I was told. I put the flag where the Union Jack had been. The crowd started to sing the '*Internationale*'.

I'm afraid my pleasure was short-lived. I heard a loud voice with a local accent shouting up at me from a loudhailer. It was a policeman.

'Eleanor Berry, will you please remove that flag and come down to the market-place.' I wondered how he knew my name.

I made the mistake of walking right to the edge of the building. An attack of vertigo took me over. It seemed as if the building had tilted itself on its side and I thought I was about to fall off it. Everything around me was spinning and I felt nauseated. I lay on my stomach, hoping the building wouldn't tilt any further.

'I told you to come down to the market-place, Eleanor Berry, bringing that flag with you,' said the policeman, 'and if you fail to obey my orders you will be brought down by force.' I was irritated by the fact that he used my first name and surname, like a schoolmistress.

I was not aware at the time of what was going on below. I was told later that someone in the crowd had given the policeman the following advice:–

'She won't respond to your orders, Officer. There's only one person with the power to get her down and that's Mr Maxwell inside.'

A few minutes later, I heard R.M.'s voice on the loudhailer. He had come out of the building, by which time he knew he had lost his seat to the nondescript Tory candidate, Bill Benyon.

'Ellie!'

I didn't answer at first because of the vertigo.

'Eleanore! Will you please do what the police are telling you to do. Take down that flag, and stop being so naughty!'

'I'll try to come down, Bob, but I've got very bad vertigo,' I shouted. I was extremely embarrassed and felt like an idiot.

'If you get vertigo, you shouldn't have gone up there in the first place. Stop being a naughty pussycat and do as you're told!'

'I'm trying to come down, Bob, honest to goodness, I am, but I can't find the ladder.'

'What the hell do you mean, you can't find the ladder?'

A foul-tempered policeman shinned up the ladder and took me down in a fireman's lift. Another policeman, with no sense of humour, removed the red flag and threw it to the ground by the ladder.

R.M. was still standing in front of the building. It was fortunate that the ladder was at the side. He called for me repeatedly, but I didn't go to the front, because I was still very nauseated and terrified of being sick in front of him. I sat on the ground at the base of the ladder.

'Was you told to go up there and replace the Union Jack with a Communist flag?' asked the first policeman to speak to me.

'No. No-one told me to do it.'

'Why did you do it, then?'

'Because I wanted to please Mr Maxwell,' I said, adding with incredible stupidity, 'I am in love with him and I'd be prepared to die for him, if necessary.'

'You don't 'alf come across some odd people these days!' said the policeman. 'Was it him who sent you up there?'

'No, it wasn't!' I replied.

R.M. continued to stand in front of the building. He looked sad and dejected. He was getting into the Labour Party campaign van. I went out of my way to attract his attention and waved the salvaged red flag in front of him. He smiled at me and said, 'Thanks, Ellie.' Once I knew I had pleased him, my nausea wore off.

R.M. stood up in the van and spoke to his supporters through the open roof. He boomed through the loudhailer.

'Thank you all for your courageous and loyal support. We are disappointed but not downhearted. We have lost a battle but not the war.'

Molly and her mother were standing near the van. The two eccentric women roused the crowd into singing 'For He's a Jolly Good Fellow'. I got into the van where Betty was sitting in the passenger seat. Arthur Leary, Chris Smith and R.M.'s youngest son, Kevin, then about ten, were also in the van. I joined them. We returned to the Wharf House to clear everything out.

Betty and I did this together, which to me affirmed my view that there were no feelings of rivalry between us. I considered that we were infatuated by the same man, and were fiercely united, like a couple of soldiers in the trenches, fighting for a divine cause.

I asked her, as delicately as possible, if I could take some of R.M.'s shirts from a drawer. She handed them to me. I still have these shirts with their sleeves extending nearly a yard beyond my hands. Sometimes, I use them as night-dresses.

Betty sang my favourite Edith Piaf song, '*Padam*', as she rolled briefs and pairs of socks into balls and folded her husband's remaining shirts. The clear-out took us about two hours.

Once it was over, R.M., Arthur Leary, Chris Smith and I got into the campaign van. Chris drove down Labour-supporting streets. R.M. was standing up, speaking through the megaphone. 'We have lost a battle but not the war,' he repeated.

I sat in the front between Chris and Arthur. Occasionally, R.M. held my hair to steady himself when he kept sitting down and standing up. This gave me a fantastic buzz. Despite the defeat, I was supremely happy during this journey, being surrounded by men with my favourite one holding my hair. Chris saw two Tories walking down the street, wearing blue rosettes and laughing. He wound down the window and leant out.

'Bloody Tories! Let it fall in and pull the sodding chain!' he shouted vulgarly.

R.M. said nothing but when I looked at him in the driver's mirror, I saw he was smiling.

We returned to the Wharf House for lunch. We went into R.M.'s study for drinks and found Mick Scrivener sitting there weeping. He rose to his feet and walked over to R.M.

'I'm so ashamed, Bob, of failing to stand up to Tim Miles.'

R.M. ruffled the weeping man's hair.

'It's all right, Mick. It's all right.'

But as he left the study to go into the dining room, I could see from his face that he regarded Scrivener with pathos and disrespect. R.M. had always hated weak, timid men. In fact, he hated nearly all men. He had a tendency to terrify men, but very rarely women.

'That poor man!' I said, turning to R.M. 'It's clear how much he admires you.'

'I understand that but he's a bit gaga.'

The lunch was a very sad occasion. Molly and her mother had tears in their eyes throughout the meal. Betty's voice was sad and flattened. R.M. said very little but cheered up when beer was provided for him.

There was a moment of comic relief when a home-made chocolate cake was brought into the room. Ghislaine, then aged nine, leant across the table and licked it. Betty ticked her off but R.M. was unable to keep a straight face when his favourite child was misbehaving.

The family and I left the house after lunch, and returned in a convoy of cars to Headington Hill Hall. I was alone with R.M. in the campaign van. During the two hours it took to drive from Milton Keynes to Oxford, I had a very long, intimate conversation with him.

'Does Michael [my father] disapprove of our relationship?' he asked suddenly. 'He'd be right to.'

'He's never mentioned it. Do you think it annoys him?'

'Yes,' said R.M.

'Why?'

'Because I'd resent it if your father carried on like this with Isabel. I'd go round to his house and put a stop to it.'

'A stop to what?'

'Use your head!'

'My father's not suspicious. He's got nothing to be suspicious about.'

'Oh, has he not? Ha ha!'

There was a short pause.

'Why were you so disturbed by the novel *Foma Gordyev*? Why did a book like that hit you so hard?' he asked.

As I see it now, Gorky's *Foma Gordyev* is a confused, repetitive, rambling book about barges combing the Volga in nineteenth-century Russia, and the rowdy behaviour of people aboard them. Looking back on it, Foma, the book's main protagonist, really is a most awful drip, who cannot relate to others and continuously passes remarks, such as, 'I'm afraid I haven't really got used to life yet.' He bumbles about, swigging, ranting at members of his own class, and for want of better words, is a shambling pain in the butt. Perhaps the book obsessed me because of its richness of language, its vibrant tone and its actual coming alive, regardless of Foma's effete nihilism. Unnecessarily extensive coverage is given to the appearance and function of the engines propelling the Volga-combing barges.

'The book haunted and tormented me,' I said.

'It haunted you? Why did it haunt you?' asked R.M.

I started shouting. He told me to stop shouting. I was not considerate enough to take the loss of his seat on board. I told him the sequence of events in *Foma Gordyev*, and went on shouting because I wanted to exorcise something I didn't understand.

'Foma Gordyev is the book's main character. He's the wealthy son of a barge owner who dies in morbid circumstances, in front of his son.' I looked at R.M. sideways. He looked baffled. I continued, 'He dies suddenly on a warm autumn morning at an outdoor table shaded by apple trees. As I understand it, he was drinking tea out of a glass, and when the wind blew more strongly, a few apples fell onto the table and occasionally into the tea.'

'I'm absolutely riveted,' said R.M., 'but go on all the same.'

'The boy never recovers from his father's death, and turns into a permanently intoxicated wreck. Though wealthy, he despises the gluttony of his own class.'

R.M. cleared his throat loudly at this point. I continued, 'The book ends very abruptly and describes the deterioration of the hero's mind. He foresees social change and claims he is a prophet. He is always in rags, rolling about in gutters, pissed.'

'What did I say just now about your shouting?' said R.M.

'Shouting?'

'Yes, shouting. I told you I didn't want to hear you shouting, didn't I?'

'Yes, I think you did.'

'So, why are you continuing to shout?'

'Sorry. I won't do it again.'

'Have you anything more to say about the contents of that book?'

'Yes. Towards the end, there's an incident, describing the hero's drunken rage about the greed of his fellow merchants. He uses wonderful language. "Even hell is too good a place for swine like you! Not in clean flames, but in sizzling dung ought you to be scorched, tormented for centuries on end." All the merchants could think of doing was to tie him up and send for his godfather.

'The book's a bit jerky, as if the author were in a hurry to finish it. Its hero staggers about, saying he can't understand himself and others around him.'

'Christ! When the hell's this story going to end?' R.M. said, adding, 'You're shouting, again. You've been shouting ever since you got into this van.'

'Oh, sorry. The book's ending is an anti-climax. The man wanders about saying he's a prophet, and someone bumping into him in the street, says, "Ha, ha, a prophet indeed"!'

'Is that the lot?' asked R.M., hopefully.

'Yes. It's the lot. That's the last sentence. It's pretty abrupt.'

'Are you still seeing all those fucking doctors?' he asked suddenly.

'No. Just Dr Carl Heinz Goldman. I only see him because I fancy him.'

'Oh, you do, do you? I'll soon see about that!'

I told him that I had had a morbid fascination for Russian literature. I thought I could handle it but I could not. In the end, it possessed me. The problem was not helped at school by my house-mistress who sometimes summoned me into her study and told me that Russian literature was damaging my mind. I might never have known this was happening, had she not tried to get into my head.

'My house-mistress called me into her study once, and said, "It has been brought to my attention that you sing the Russian National Anthem in your bath",' I told R.M. spontaneously.

'Did you sing the Russian National Anthem in your bath?' he asked, his tone totally baffled.

'Oh, yes, yes, I did. Oh, I forgot to tell you, the father went into his son's room and told him he was about to die.'

'Whose bloody father?'

'Foma Gordyev's father.'

'You seem to be very preoccupied with death. I think you lost someone you loved very much. Is that what happened?' he asked.

'No.'

'I think I know why that book disturbed you. I'm quite familiar with it. You certainly didn't advertise it very interestingly. What hit you was its profound purity and richness of language. You loved the book so much that I bet you read it over and over again, and each time, you found more beauty and purity than the time before. So much beauty and purity did you see, that life itself disappointed you. You couldn't reconcile yourself to reality after reading it. Your life became sad and humdrum. You're rather a lonely person, aren't you?'

'Sometimes, I am. Not always.'

'You came out of yourself when you were working for us. Everyone loved you being there. You spend too much time on your own. You need company. I know what loneliness is like. I'm going to write a book about it one day. Have you ever thought of getting married? Have you ever been in love?'

64

'Well, er, well not yet,' I said.

'To make a marriage work, you have to give as much as you take. Which are you, a giver or a taker? You're sexy enough to have men running after you in droves.'

'I'd say I was both of them,' I said abruptly. 'Most of us are.'

'Sometimes I think you should have been born a male,' he said suddenly.

'If I had been, our relationship wouldn't have been the way it is. I know you don't always get on very well with other men,' I said (tactfully).

Another guttural Cossack's laugh. A rather uncomfortable silence. All I hear is his slow breathing.

'Where did you go to school?' he asked.

I named my school

'Isn't that the school which is notorious for forcing excessive religious instruction onto its girls?'

'Yes.'

'That must have put you off religion for life.'

'It did.'

'There's a lay-by on the left. You want me to pull into the side and stop the van, don't you?'

'Yes.'

'Are you all right?'

'Yes.'

'Do you want some water?'

'No.'

'You're very hot. You shouldn't be wearing a thick leather jacket in June. It will make you feel ill.'

'It's OK.'

'No, it isn't. Take it off.'

I laughed nervously.

'It's not funny. If you don't take it off, I'll do so for you.'

I went on laughing.

'Stop your silly giggling. Do you do that when you're with Carl Heinz Goldman?'

'Sometimes.'

'We once had an altercation, he and I. What does he say about me?' asked R.M.

'He doesn't talk about you very much.'

'I think he does. Relax, will you! You're like a board. Would

65

you prefer him to be sitting here instead of me?'

'No!'

'Come on. Get that bloody thing off.'

* * *

'I had an unfortunate experience with Goldman's wife,' I said later. 'I didn't know who she was. I thought she was a temporary receptionist.'

'What did you say to her?'

'I said, "Christ, that man Goldman's attractive! He must come like the Volga!"'

R.M. let out another guttural Cossack's laugh. 'I should imagine he'd be a case of *Quiet Flows the Don*, more likely. That was what you might call putting your foot in it,' he said.

The rest of the conversation took place in Russian. By the time we got to Headington Hill Hall, R.M., whose eardrums must have been perforated by my manic shouting, was exhausted and slept until dinner.

Ghislaine came up to me in the hall and pointed to her suitcase.

'Will you take this up to my room, please,' she said.

'No, I will not. I'm not your maid.'

'Will you come up and push me on my rocking horse?'

'I'll do that if it's what you want.'

While I was pushing her, she said suddenly, 'I don't think you're Labour at all. I think you're a Tory.

'Why?'

'I've just heard things. I know you went to London on Polling Day, and I think you voted Conservative.'

'You can think anything you want.'

'Just tell me. I won't repeat it. Did you vote Conservative?'

'No', I lied. 'Anyway, it's time for dinner.'

Kevin came into the room to say dinner had started. He briefed me on what was being discussed at dinner. There was a clinical formality in the way he spoke, accompanied by a dry sense of humour. He was intellectually advanced for a 10-year-old child, sharp, intuitive and concise. I couldn't make him out. Also, he got rather cross at breakfast the next morning because there were no Rice Krispies.

'You're late,' said R.M. as I sat down in the vacant chair on his left.

'Yes, I know. Ghislaine wanted me to play with her in her bedroom.'

'It is not Ghislaine who gives the orders in this house. It's her father,' said R.M. I could tell that he was feeling depressed.

'I'm sorry, Bob. I promise I won't be late again.'

Ghislaine walked round to him and asked him to pull a wishbone with her. She got the wish and he asked her what it was.

'I made a wish that you would win next time,' she said.

He took her on his knee and caressed her. This made me irrationally jealous.

When R.M. was subdued, it was not uncommon for his children to be infected by his mood. Sometimes, he would break the silence by putting very sudden questions to anyone around him. On a few occasions, I was the recipient of one of these questions but I always barked at him and that made him laugh.

Jean, sitting on R.M.'s right, made some comment about the Common Market, implying that she favoured the country's integration into a united Europe. R.M. turned to me.

'Eleanore, does that support your view?'

'No, it doesn't. By that criterion, a nation is robbed of its indivi-duality and it becomes a mere county within a soulless state.' (I realized I was shouting again.)

R.M. looked a bit startled by my tone of voice and then he smiled.

There was an interval in the conversation. The children talked among themselves for a while until Betty entered the conversation.

'What are we going to do about that heinous Tim Miles, Papa? Not only has he lost you your seat through sheer idleness. He also bullied a very honest and conscientious man, causing him to have a nervous breakdown.'

'I ought to have sent Eleanore round to him. She would have scared the living wits out of him. Eleanore's very sexy, particularly when she wears her leather!' said R.M.

He had finished eating and sprang to his feet.

'All right. Dinner's over,' he said. The family got up and shuffled out.

For the first and only time during our relationship, I had a 'bite' from R.M. later on that evening. He, likewise, received one or two from me. One of these occurred years later in July 1983 when I was suffering from Valium withdrawal and thought I was dying of a brain tumour. I will come to that later.

After the post-election dinner, Betty took me up to a television room, known as the 'bird room' because of the large collection of porcelain birds in there. Betty showed me some family albums. Lying loose in one of them were some chest X-rays. I thought this was strange and I asked Betty whose they were and what they showed.

'They're Bob's X-rays. He had a lung removed.'

I knew about this already and couldn't think of anything appropriate to say. 'Did he now?' I eventually muttered.

Interestingly, Betty showed the album to my mother once, and drew her attention to the X-rays.

'I must say, I really do think that putting X-rays in a photograph album, is *awfully* odd,' commented my mother.

Betty went to bed and R.M. came into the room and said there was an American thriller he wanted to watch. He asked me if I wanted to see it and I said I did. He sat on the sofa and I sat on the floor at his feet.

The film was incomprehensible. Even when my wits are at their best, I find American accents, particularly with voices speaking very fast, difficult to understand.

However, R.M. appeared to understand the film and he found it extremely gripping. I started asking a lot of questions as is my habit during films. If I go to the cinema unaccompanied, I call for the usherette in the same way I would call for a taxi. I make her sit beside me and tell me what's going on. I give her 50p for every 'what did he say?' and £1 for every 'what is he doing?'.

'Who's that man, Bob?'

Silence.

'Is he going to murder that woman?'

Silence.

'Is that the woman he's been taking out?'

Silence.

'Is that the woman's sister?'

Silence.

'I don't understand. Are they identical twins?'

It was at that point that I had my bite.

'How the fucking hell should I know!' he bellowed. 'You can see the film just as well as I can so shut up!'

'Yes, Bob.'

I made a mental note of the fact that R.M. would not make a very co-operative cinema usherette.

The next day, I came down wearing a red leather miniskirt and patent high-heeled boots, covering part of the thigh. I had coffee. Then I went into R.M.'s study where I knew he would be working. He seemed delighted to see me, either because of my apparel or my personality, probably both.

'Pamela rang earlier,' he said a little irritably. 'She wants you back. I don't want you to go. I'm going to miss you and I want you to come back here whenever you feel like it. You have a permanent invitation to my house, even if you only want to call in for one of your baths. By the way, that fiery old driver's waiting for you outside, Mr Lightweight or Brightwell, or whatever his silly name is.'

'You're so kind,' I said. 'I really don't want to leave.'

'I'm not kind! There are a lot of untrustworthy people around who will only be interested in you because your father owns the *Telegraph*. I take you for what you are as a person and any time you have a problem, come straight to me. When you come back, we'll read *Pravda* together.

'Come and kiss me goodbye,' he said, adding, 'Thank you so much for all your hard work. We've helped each other. I've helped you become more self-assertive and aggressive and you've gone out of your way, trying to help me retain my seat. You will write to me, won't you?'

'Yes, of course I will.'

I felt very sad. I said goodbye to Betty and what children I could find. Then I went out to Mr Brightwell. R.M. waved goodbye until the car was out of sight.

5

I returned to the Maxwells on my own invitation three weeks later. It was a Friday night and R.M. had already gone to bed because he was exhausted.

Betty, some of the children and I were having breakfast in the kitchen overlooking the lawn. In came R.M., so obviously pleased to see me that it seemed as if he had been happily anticipating my visit for several days.

'Why didn't you tell me Eleanore was coming?' he said to Betty. 'If you'd told me before, I would have been able to look forward to it.' He often said this when I came to say, and my memory of his words is sacred.

It's on remembering words like that, that I become homicidal when I hear anyone criticizing R.M.. The ordeal I had to bear was even worse after his death than in his lifetime, because the press took advantage of the fact that the dead can't be libelled.

He took me for a walk round the garden and we spoke in Russian. The swimming pool was no longer in use. Its leaf-covered water was an uninviting shade of green.

Suddenly, he picked me up and held me over the water, threatening to drop me. The incident showed me the prankish side of his nature which manifested itself whenever he wanted to become the child, Lajbi, again, the boy deprived of clothes, food, toys and jokes during his appallingly unhappy childhood.

He took me to his study where Jean was waiting for him. Jean and I greeted each other before R.M. gave her instructions.

'How many people have died in the constituency, Miss Baddeley?' asked R.M.

'Only four, Mr Maxwell. I've sent the format letters to the appropriate next of kin with your signature on them.'

'Good. Any marriages for congratulations?'

'Yes, just one. The couple are ex-circus performers. The man's working in a bank now.'

'His name?'

'Cyril Dibbs. He's a dwarf.'

R.M. sat back in his executive leather chair and lit a cigar.

'And his wife, is she also a dwarf?'

'Yes, Mr Maxwell.'

'Blimey! said R.M.

The family had acquired a really singular butler whose real name I can't remember. R.M. addressed him as 'Genius' so I'll refer to him as that.

Genius came into my bedroom at 8.30 a.m. one weekend, without knocking on the door. I had reformed my habit of getting up just before lunch and he found me naked. I was just about to go to the bathroom.

'Have you got any empty glasses in here?' asked Genius.

'No. I'm getting dressed for breakfast.'

'I'll leave the room, then,' he said after an awkward pause.

'Thank you. I think that would be the best thing to do in the circumstances.' Poor old Genius. I thought it would be unfair to report him as he could not have been aware of my new early morning routine.

R.M. came down later and interviewed a blonde secretary in his study. Kevin entered the room with a glass in his hand, mistaking the blonde woman, who had her back to him, for me.

'Have a glass of wine,' he said exuberantly. 'Vintage Château de Sade!'

'Oh fuck off, Kevin!' said R.M.

'I liked the sexy blonde secretary you interviewed, Dad,' said Ian at dinner. 'She seemed much better than the one with the acne and the awful legs.'

R.M. turned on his son.

'I don't want to hear that kind of talk, Ian. It's cruel.'

'Sorry, Dad.'

I admit that I did not distinguish myself at Headington Hill Hall that weekend. On Sunday morning, I got up very late and found R.M. walking across the hall.

'Hullo. I hear you got up very early this morning,' he said.

Another weekend, when I thought I could get away with repeating the same misdemeanour, his reaction was tougher. It was about 12.45. I came into the drawing room where R.M. and the family were having pre-lunch drinks. He always served the drinks from behind the bar, like a publican.

71

'May I have a gin and tonic, please, Bob?'

He came out from behind the bar and walked with me to the other end of the room, away from everyone else.

'You must get up in the mornings,' he said, his voice raised in anger. 'Do you realize the maid was unable to come in and make the bed?'

There was something inexplicably comical about his last sentence. I imagined a timid, cowering woman, carrying dusters, mops and cloths in a bucket, waiting outside, afraid to knock on the door.

I smiled, took his hand in mine and kissed it and rolled my eyes at him. 'Forgive me, Bob.' He softened.

'Naughty pussycat,' he said, 'come over and have your gin and tonic.'

Jean Baddeley entered the room to remind R.M. that he had to go out on business that afternoon. He was dressed in a red and white pin-striped suit. Apart from his terrifying father, Jean was the only person who could control him.

'Mr Maxwell, I'm not going anywhere with you until you change into a more appropriate suit! The one you are wearing is extremely vulgar.'

'All right, all right, Miss Baddeley. I'm always being ordered about by hens.'

When I returned to London, I sent twenty red roses to Betty with a note attached, saying I was sorry I had failed to let the maid in to make the bed.

* * *

The Maxwells invited me again for the weekend six weeks later. I was walking in the garden on Saturday morning and saw Ghislaine running towards me.

'Can you do me a great favour and drive me to the stables?'

'I don't see why not. Where are they?'

'In the country, ten miles away from here. Is your car the silver one?'

'Yes.' We went to the car. 'We'll have to get a move on, otherwise, we'll be late for lunch,' I said.

'This is a nice car.'

'Yes, it's not bad. Jump in.'

72

Once she was in the passenger's seat and I had moved up the drive, she turned to me abruptly.

'By the way, Daddy said you're not to play the choral movement of Beethoven's Ninth when you're driving, because he says you have a lot of accidents, drive far too fast and crash into the backs of other cars when you listen to it. Otherwise, he said you're not too bad a driver.'

I thought she was rather impertinent and suddenly wondered whether she had asked her parents if I could drive her.

'Does your father know I'm taking you to the stables?'

'No. I never asked him.'

I did an emergency stop.

'Do you mean you asked me to take you off the premises without his permission?'

'Yes. I don't always ask his permission when I want to do things.'

'Is that because you think he might say no?'

'I suppose you could say that.'

I was furious with her for inviting me to get into an invidious position.

'It's extremely naughty and irresponsible of you, Ghislaine, to trick me into taking you off the premises. You are your father's property and if you were to come to harm, I would be answerable for it.'

I reversed down the ramp-infested, sinuous drive and came to a halt.

'Get out of the car, Ghislaine, and go into the house and ask your father's permission.'

She got out. She looked pretty and sultry with her long brown pony-tail, and large, angry almond-shaped eyes.

'It's OK. I don't want to go now,' she said.

'You've been very kind, Bob,' I said at the end of the weekend.

'I'm not kind!' His tone was almost angry. I was always telling him how kind he was and he invariably gave me the same backhandedly touching answer.

He often saw my father at press meetings in London.

'How's that smashing daughter of yours, Michael?' he said on one of these occasions, and once when he saw Nicky in London, he told him he was my surrogate father.

I never failed to look forward to my weekends at Headington Hill Hall.

R.M. was in rather a low mood one day at lunch. Genius, who found it extremely difficult to tell the difference between red wine and port, poured port into the high-stemmed, intricately decorated Venetian glasses. R.M. got very irritated.

'Oh, no, no, no, no, Genius!' he shouted. 'This is port. We want wine!'

Genius went out and produced a bottle of wine and a tray of clean glasses during the cheese course. The unfortunate man bungled again.

R.M. had ordered more glasses so that the cheaper wine could be supplemented by a more costly wine, a crate of which had been delivered to the house by a friend of the family.

Genius poured the costly wine into glasses still containing the ordinary wine. R.M. was furious.

'No, no, no, no, no, Genius!' he repeated, this time more angrily than the first.

'I'm sorry, Mr Maxwell, I don't understand your instructions.'

'Just take away all the glasses and start again!'

R.M. suffered from unnerving mood swings, ranging from playful euphoria to impenetrable gloom. Until the day he died, he had memories of his family being herded on to trains bound for the gas chambers. Added to this, he was secretly ashamed of his terror of his father.

His greatest childhood love was for his mother, Hannah Hoch. I saw a picture of her once. She closely resembled Isabel's twin sister, Christine, except that she was stouter. In the picture, she wore a simple, dark-coloured dress with a large collar. Her face had a look of Mona Lisa serenity. R.M., known to her as Lajbi, was her favourite child and I could imagine him running behind her everywhere she went, clinging to her skirts.

'I love hiding behind ladies' petticoats,' he once said to me at lunch when he was in a relaxed mood. I hated it when he was depressed, fearing old age and loneliness, fearing the loss of his daughters when they would eventually marry, fearing recessions and bankruptcy and the possible demise of his loved ones. I'm sure he often looked back to the death of his oldest son, Michael, whom he wanted to succeed him and who lay in a coma for several years before he died.

Most of all, his horrendous memories of the Holocaust haunted him all his life and even the presence of his wife and children, was sometimes incapable of lifting the black cloud from his mind.

When in these moods he seldom spoke and did not welcome any conversational overtures. Sometimes, he would unconsciously interrogate a family member within earshot and ask one of his arresting questions, of which, for some unknown reason, Ghislaine, his favourite, was often the recipient.

He seldom did this to me when he was in one of these moods but he did question me one day when I was sitting next to him. I can tell when someone near me is depressed, whether they show it or not. That day, R.M. definitely was, even though he had recently won £50,000 from a lawsuit against *Private Eye*. I decided not to speak until he spoke to me because it is hard to handle a depressed person.

Lunch was almost silent. I felt very sad to see R.M. looking so tired. He had put on some weight, although his facial beauty was still intact. He turned to me very suddenly, speaking quite quietly.

'Tell me, Eleanore, when you're not looking ravishingly beautiful, how do you occupy your time?'

The compliment was like an elixir. I thanked him but he only wanted a concise answer.

'I work for agencies who send me to London hospitals where I follow the surgeons on ward rounds. I write down everything they say about the patients they see, log it into a computer and enter it into their files. Sometimes, I am sent to the post mortem room to take notes during autopsies.'

'No gory talk, please,' said R.M.

'Papa, she's been doing that for years and years,' said Betty to him from across the table. 'Do you know what she said? She said she had been out of work for two whole days. I had to laugh.'

'I don't see why,' said R.M. 'Two days are two days lost.'

'I went for an interview, which I failed,' I said. 'I was interviewed by a dreadful obstetrician in one of London's hospitals. He was a weirdo. He said, "Are you happy?"'

'"No, of course I'm not happy, you fool! I'm out of bloody work, aren't I?" I said.'

R.M. was so amused, it seemed as if my story had lifted his depression. 'How much are you getting now?' he asked.

The rate was £9.50 an hour.

'I get £13.50 an hour,' I said. 'I wouldn't settle for less than that.'

'Good! You could take us all out to dinner at the Ritz with

that,' he said.

I was feeling a bit better because his black mood had shifted.

'Bob, will you give me a signed copy of your book about the *Private Eye* case – *Malice in Wonderland*?'

R.M. picked up a leg of chicken with his fingers and shoved it into his mouth.

'I don't see why not. You gave me a signed copy of *Never Alone with Rex Malone*. Do you remember?'

'I don't forget the titles of my books easily,' I said.

He laughed again.

'Of course I'll sign it for you – as one author to another.'

He got up abruptly from the table and went over to his oldest surviving son, Philip.

'Come on, Philip,' he said, 'there's work to do,' and disappeared through the door dividing the dining room from the drawing room. Compulsively, I got up and followed the father and son. I had a burning urge to talk to R.M., even if I had no idea what I wanted to talk to him about.

R.M. tried to close the door, but because I had taken Speed, my behaviour was very manic and irrational. I had taken a palmful of the stuff, to give myself a maximum mental and physical buzz. Had I not taken it, I would not have displayed such appalling manners and lack of consideration for others.

He was closing the door but I threw my weight against it.

'Bob, I'm not leaving here until you give me a signed copy of your book. Open the door!' I shouted.

'Goodbye!' he said. He and Philip were sitting down, talking shop. I was irritated. I wasn't prepared to leave until he had given me what I wanted.

The Speed robbed me of all my inhibitions. I threw my weight against the door. I banged on it, shouting, 'Open this door!' He opened it, looking amused and astonished.

'Blimey, I like your resistance!' he said.

He led me in by the hand, just as an adult holds on to a child crossing a road. We went into the study next to the drawing room. He took the book from the top of a pile and wrote a friendly, but not particularly interesting message in it, followed by his signature.

'There you are, Missy.'

I thanked him and held the book to my chest.

76

'Turn round. Let's have a look at you.'

I did as he asked. I was wearing a yellow leather suit and a pair of red snake-skin stiletto boots for which he had expressed a liking on other occasions. He liked my collection of leather suits so I wore one of them every time I saw him, except during heatwaves.

'You look smashing!' he said.

Yet another elixir. I rolled my eyes at him and put my arms round his neck while he kissed me on the mouth.

'You're a rare man, Bob,' I said. After about half an hour, I left. I felt euphoric for hours afterwards.

Euphoric though I might have felt, my pleasure was interspersed with black thoughts. I had lied about the moneys I was receiving, because I wanted to Impress R.M. How I wished to go back to his office, throw myself at his feet and shout, 'Whip me, Master, for I am a coward!'

This was the first masochistic fantasy I had had in my life.

* * *

My visits to the house were frequent. This time, I went there for lunch one stifling hot Saturday in July. I was going through a phase of Valium addiction and my doctor at that time, with whom I got on very badly, refused to wean me off the drug. Instead, he stopped prescribing it.

Physically, I felt iller than I had ever felt in my life. A gong seemed to be booming inside my head. I felt dizzy and faint. I was sweating so much that my clothes were clinging to me like limpets. Accompanied by these symptoms were anxiety and shakes.

I didn't realize the addictive properties of Valium. I had been taking 50–100 mg a night for insomnia and was forced to stop abruptly. I assumed I had a brain tumour. I felt that I was on the way out and I had a yearning to see the Maxwells first.

When I got to the gates of the house, guarded by an over-vigilant watchman, he found my voice so strange that he had to phone through to R.M. to see if I could come in.

Once I arrived at the house, I had a drink, first with Ian, who had to represent his father at someone's funeral. Then I had another drink with Betty. I wondered whether to tell Ian, who was still in the room, that I felt ill but decided not to. I thought the alcohol would drain my symptoms. I could have told Betty, but she would have made a fuss and put me to bed.

'Have another,' said Ian.

'I'd better not. I'll only go under.'

'Don't worry. You won't go under. I can guarantee that.' I tried to believe him. My main fear was that I was going to drop dead in front of him.

Betty left the room briefly and came back just as Ian was leaving. I couldn't see her in focus and struggled to disguise my condition. She talked at length about numerous subjects including the activities of her children, her visits to Val d'Isère and R.M.'s dissatisfaction with Ghislaine's lifestyle. Ghislaine was now in her early 20s, and R.M. and she had different views on morality.

'Where's Bob now?' I asked.

'He's in the garden. We'll go and find him.'

We left the house and went into the garden. I could hardly walk. I held Betty's arm.

We found R.M. His mood was relaxed. He was looking at the flowers.

'I'm interviewing a man here this afternoon,' he said, 'a man who is an authority on Sloane Rangers. Would you like to meet him?'

'Oh, Christ! Do I have to?' I shouted.

The tension was broken. There were times when R.M. appeared to like women shouting at him and he roared with laughter.

'Hey, I liked that,' he said. 'We're having lunch in a minute. Come and sit next to me.'

By this time I felt so ill that I thought I was going to die. I have always believed it to be the height of bad manners to die, either in someone's house or their garden, and I hoped that if the Reaper wanted to take me, he would be considerate enough to do so once I had got back to London.

R.M., Jean and Betty came and took their seats at the table. It was overbearingly hot eating in the garden and there were no umbrellas. R.M. wolf-whistled for Oping, the cook, which made me laugh out loud.

'What are you laughing at?' he asked.

'I like the way you whistled. My sister whistles like that but I don't know how to do it.'

I knew that if the conversation continued in English, I'd probably be able to hold out. There was comic relief when the family dog, Angara, named after a Czechoslovakian river, forced its way under the glass table and licked Oping's legs when she was serving.

R.M. pulled back his chair.

'Do you think we could get the dog out?' he said.

Jean talked at length about sheets and pillowcases and linen and laundry. I was relieved not to have to speak because even my tongue was aching and my mouth and throat felt like sand.

'All right, all right, Jean,' said R.M. 'Poor Eleanore doesn't want to sit here while you talk about sheets, and I haven't seen her for ages. Come on, Eleanore, let's have some comic relief. Tell me about your outrageous adventures.'

I did my best to amuse R.M. but feared he would notice my impediment. For a mam who insisted on concise conversation, he was remarkably patient that day. I was determined to make him laugh but heard the slurred drone in my voice. I told him the following:

I said my first job was that of a nanny but that I was sacked after ten minutes. I'd done a lot of work as a commercial translator, which bored me stiff.

Then I found work as a verbal translator, i.e. an interpreter, dealing with non-English speaking hospital patients. I couldn't pull this off. I got agitated all the time and shouted everything at the top of my voice. I was bunged out.

After that, I took shorthand for pathologists, to fuel my morbidity. A senior secretary in one of the many hospitals I was sent to actually asked me to take her dress to the cleaners.

'Jesus, I wouldn't like to have been her! What the hell did you say to her, Basso Profundo?' asked R.M.

'I said: "Take it to the cleaners, your bloody self! I'm not your lackey!"'

'Christ turned the other cheek, so why couldn't you?' said R.M. expressing an attitude I felt totally out of character.

'Christ died young,' I said. R.M. looked shocked for some reason and tilted his head backwards, pursing his lips, which he always did when he was displeased or disquieted. I smiled at him to regain his favour.

'Your stories are killing me. Let's have some more, but for Christ's sake, keep them brief!'

'I went to a personnel department one Monday morning and a personnel officer casually told me I'd been double-booked.'

79

'I hope you hit her on the head with a shoe,' said R.M.

'I should have done. Instead, I said, "Would you say that to a taxi driver?"

"No," she said.

"I'm sure you wouldn't. Shall I tell you why."

"Why?"

"Because a taxi driver would slit your throat. So would I if I had a knife." '

I was getting iller in the heat. It's said to be bad manners to drop dead in someone's home. I shuddered.

Oping came to the table to tell R.M. a call had come through from Moscow but he wanted to finish the conversation first.

'All right, so the next day I take it you went back with your knife.'

These words were going round and round in my head like a bee.

'Eleanore, are you all right?' said Betty.

'I'm afraid I've got a bit of sunstroke. I forgot to bring a hat.'

'Don't worry. You can lie on the sofa with a bandage round your eyes. It will soon wear off. I'll give you some Paracetamol.'

I was there for two hours. The Valium withdrawal was no better.

'You've been very kind,' I said to Betty, 'but I must go back to London now.'

'Are you OK to drive?'

'Of course.'

My symptoms were still just as bad and if anything, worse still.

'I do feel ever so much better now,' I lied. 'Besides, I've got a sick relative I promised to have tea with and she hasn't got a telephone.'

'All right,' said Betty, 'as long as you're OK.'

I drove back to London in the slow lane all the way with four windows open.

I booked myself into the London clinic, for which I am insured, and sent for a solicitor to make out a Will. I remained there for six weeks and was in bed all day, except on an occasion when I had to have a brain scan and be pushed down the street in a wheelchair. Sometimes I needed Valium so badly that all I could do was thrash backwards and forwards, screaming. My head was so heavy I couldn't hold it up and my hair was tangled and unbrushed. I looked the epitome of Rochester's wife.

After six weeks, the symptoms stopped. The Valium withdrawal was complete. My friends and relatives who visited me, remarked irritatingly that I was a hypochondriac. Thanks a lot!

* * *

I completed the manuscript of *Never Alone with Rex Malone* in the summer of 1985. The book opened in 2054 and looked back to the late twentieth century when R.M. and Betty, known as Rex Malone and Hortense Malone respectively, were the most revered couple in Britain. A thuggish funeral director called Natalie Klein, modelled loosely on myself, fought ruthlessly and unscrupulously for them in any way she could.

I knew I couldn't send it to the publisher until R.M. had found out about it. I was terrified he would refuse to let me publish it because of the morbidity, extreme ribaldry and manic black humour which peppered its pages.

I asked my unfortunate father if he would read the manuscript of the book and he agreed to do so. Illogically, my main motive for asking him was fear that, because of the reasons given, R.M. would find it too black for me to publish it. It was my need for reassurance that prompted me to ask my father for his opinion.

My father and I had what the Kray Twins would have called 'a little bit of an argument'. My father was strongly against the idea of my deification of R.M.

'You've built a bloody great gold effigy of the man, as if he was Christ!' he complained, his voice raised, adding, 'If this book is to be a commercial venture, Rex Malone should not be recognizable as Maxwell, but should be an amalgamation of characters, starting with Sir Winston Churchill!'

'I understand what you say, but if I leave Rex Malone as he is, is there any reason why Bob would be upset?'

'No! The man would be tickled pink!' said my father forcefully.

I did not take my father's advice.

I started to get *Rex Malone* moving. I rang Ian (R.M.'s son) in his flat at the Barbican.

'Ian, I've got something very important to tell you,' I said in a voice which might have suggested all my relatives had been killed in a plane crash.

'Well tell me, then. Why all this hassle?'

'I've just written a book in which your father is the main

character. I've made him out to be a national hero, who becomes emotionally involved with a funeral director.'

Ian was taken aback and didn't speak straight away.

'Hullo, Ian, are you there?'

'Yes. This man in your book – is he recognizable as Bob?' (I was interested that he did not say 'my father.')

'Oh Christ, yes! Your father must see it, though, before I send it off.'

'I don't know why you're so worried. I'm going to stay with him this weekend. Why don't you send the manuscript round to me in a taxi and I'll take it to him? What are you calling him?'

'Rex Malone.'

'Jesus!'

I sent the manuscript to Ian, having rubbed some of its pages with heather given to me by a gypsy (I'm incurably superstitious). Ian said he'd ring me after the weekend. I was so nervous that R.M. would think the book too macabre, that I spent Saturday and Sunday in bed.

Ian's call came through early on Monday morning.

'Is it all right?' I asked hysterically.

'Of course, it's all right,' he said. 'I gave the book to Dad to read and also read aloud to him the passages I thought he'd missed.'

'What did he say?'

'He was extraordinarily flattered and amused. He had a good laugh. He wants you to come down next Saturday.'

'When on Saturday and until when?'

'Twelve noon. We're having some of Anne's friends for lunch. You can stay for dinner if you want.'

On Saturday, I put on a turquoise shirt and matching turquoise trousers, tucked into the red snake-skin stiletto-heeled boots.

I drove, reaching speeds of 110 miles per hour down the M40, in a state of euphoria. As I came closer to Oxford, I felt exhausted. I pulled in and took what I thought were five Speed pills.

Instead, I took five Maxalon, as the two bottles and the pills looked similar. Maxalon, taken in such a quantity, induces terrifying gloom which can last for two weeks. It hit me twenty minutes after I'd swallowed it and I couldn't understand what was wrong.

I got to the Maxwells', having called at a pub for liquor which wasn't strong enough to lift the self-inflicted gloom. Oping opened the door for me.

'Hullo,' I said. 'How are you keeping?'

'Very well, very well, thank you, Eleanore. Mr Maxwell is waiting for you. He wants to see you.'

'Where is he?'

'On the lawn.'

I started to get very hot and agitated. I panicked and went upstairs and took a bath.

I found R.M. at a table outside, accompanied by Jean, Ghislaine and a strange-looking, heavily sweating man in black, talking about prayer books. Ghislaine and Bob were quarrelling because he said her dress was indecent and she was threatening to pour a bowl of strawberries over his head. His attention was distracted.

'There you are!' he said to me. 'Oping told me you'd arrived half an hour ago. What did you do before you came outside?'

'My hands were covered in oil. I had to go upstairs and scrub it off.'

He raised his head and pursed his lips which he always did when he knew he was being lied to.

'Well, whatever you did, you look smashing and it's nice to see you again. By the way, I know all about your book. I've read it.'

'Indeed? Did you enjoy it?'

'Yes, it was a good laugh. I didn't know what had hit me. I was absolutely flabbergasted!'

The main reason R.M. was 'flabbergasted', was that he had read a passage showing his representative, Rex Malone, picking up a dead body, slinging it over his shoulder to give a Brownie his autograph, before throwing it into a hearse, during a general election campaign.

'I showed my father the book,' I said, 'and I am a little confused as to what to do. My father said I was to make Rex Malone an amalgamation.'

'What the hell do you mean, an amalgamation?'

'Well, he said Rex Malone should not be recognizable as you.'

'Oh that's all right. There's no need to worry. Don't take any notice of your Dad! Leave Rex Malone just as he is.'

I later told my father that I had been forbidden to tamper with Malone and that my doing so would upset R.M. and his family. I thought I smoothed things over very skilfully.

Ghislaine interrupted the conversation which annoyed me because I thought R.M. was going to say more.

'Do you know something, Eleanor? My father is being an absolute pain.'

'I'm afraid that's none of my business,' I said.

R.M. and Ghislaine started wrestling. I became very bored. I was furious with myself for taking the wrong pills. I turned to Jean and made amicable conversation with her. R.M. left the table to have his rest. There was a strong overhead sun, but when he left, I felt it had gone behind a cloud. I waited all afternoon for him to come back and, to pass the time, I talked to the guests and went swimming.

R.M. returned at six, wearing a white towelling dressing gown and sat down. I kissed Betty goodbye and then knelt at R.M.'s feet and let him take my hand in his. I waited for him to kiss me goodbye.

'Goodbye, Missy, and good luck with your book. Remember – don't take any notice of your Dad.'

6

I visited the house again. R.M. landed by helicopter a few feet away from the lunch table in the garden. His timing was immaculate. He arrived just as the food was being put on the table. He greeted me in his usual affectionate, friendly way, but seemed irritated by my putting my fingers in my ears to protect them from the whirring rotor blades.

Betty and Jean and a strange-looking young man who never spoke, even to say good-morning, had taken their places at the table.

I had noted over the years that R.M. saved all his charms and flirtatious chivalry for female company which is why women found him irresistible. However, this pattern of social conduct was rarely directed towards members of his own sex, which is why men very frequently disliked him and many women adulated him.

The pilot turned the helicopter rotor off. R.M. stood still, while the stranger remained glued to his chair, looking at the plate of fresh salmon which had been placed in front of him. I sensed R.M. was in another depression and that his mood was poor. He directed his piercing black eyes at the younger man.

'Who are you?' he demanded. His tone was hostile.

The man didn't answer. Nor did he rise to his feet when his host addressed him. The question was repeated at a shout and the man still failed to answer. I got the giggles.

'Who's he?' said R.M. to me.

'Your guess is as good as mine. He's been sitting in silence all morning and I couldn't get his name out of him, for love nor money. Maybe he's an escaped Trappist monk.'

I turned to the man.

'You really must say who you are and rise to your feet when your host addresses you. Tell him your name.'

Finally, the stranger answered although I can't remember the name he gave.

'Why are you here?' asked R.M., still standing while his guest remained seated.

'I'm here because you asked me to come here,' said the man.

'I don't remember asking you. How do you earn your keep?'

'I'm on the *Mirror*,' said the man while I struggled to keep a straight face. 'It was you who interviewed me last week.'

R.M. sat down between Jean and Betty. For some incomprehensible reason, he addressed the stranger in French which he spoke with a thick East European accent.

'What have you learned since joining the *Mirror*?' he asked impatiently, strangely addressing him as '*tu*'.

The man bumbled on and on in a monotonous, sleep-inducing voice. I dreaded to think what his prose would be like, if he were called upon to write for the *Mirror*.

R.M. sometimes tended to get a bit rough when he was depressed, although, with a few exceptions, women were immune to the sharper side of his tongue.

'I want to ask you a question, Bob,' I said, calling across the table.

'All right. What's your question?'

'A film producer says he's interested in making a film of *Never Alone with Rex Malone*. I said I'd have to ask your permission first. Do you give me your permission or not?'

'I give you my entire permission. Any idea who's going to play me?'

'They want to get Ben Gazzara to do it. He's American but Peter O'Toole could dub your voice because his accent is not at all unlike yours. B.G.'s very good. Do you approve of him?'

Bob finished his huge mouthful of salmon, peas and boiled potatoes and took a slug of Chablis to wash them down.

'No,' he said. (I suspected he hadn't heard of this actor.)

'Why? He's very attractive.'

'No, he isn't!'

'No normal man finds another man attractive. Women go mad when they see him.'

'I don't care whether they go mad or not. What's wrong with Robert Mitchum?'

'Nothing, but I don't have the last decision. There's another question I need to ask you. There's a possibility that *Never Alone with Rex Malone* will be reprinted. May I please quote you as saying you were "absolutely flabbergasted" by it when I saw you in July 1985?'

'Yes.'

'May I also quote you as having said you just didn't know what had hit you, which you said the last time we met?'

'No.'

The silent young man entered the conversation at this point. I was amazed that he was capable of speaking spontaneously.

'Mr Maxwell, I'm told the Head of the Ethiopian Government presented you with a silver cup, engraved with an acknowledgement of your kindness and generosity towards the famine victims.'

R.M. put two fingers in each side of his mouth and gave one of his wolf-whistles. Genius hurried to the table with his hands clasped in front of him. He seemed a combination of Lurch from *The Addams Family* and the enigmatic, mute lackey from *Waiting for Godot*.

'What can I do for you, Mr Maxwell?'

'There's a silver cup with an engraving on it, on the shelf in the library area next door to the drawing room. Bring it to the table.'

Genius scuttled off. He spent a long time looking for the cup which indicated that it was somewhere else. He came to the table, his head lowered as if mounting the steps of a scaffold.

'It's not where you said it was, Mr Maxwell.'

R.M. looked exasperated. He rose from his chair and walked towards the house with Genius following him attentively.

The cup was not where R.M. had said it was. It was in one of the offices. He brought it back to the table with Genius still following him.

'It wasn't your fault, Genius,' he said, 'so you can dry your tears.'

The cup was shown to the tongueless guest who managed only to make obsequious comments about the engraving.

R.M. saw through him, his artifice and no doubt his fear. It was clear he despised him. In this case, the man should have asserted himself and shown his disdain for his host, instead of sucking up to him. It is true R.M. had been rude to him, but I did not think this called for abject cowardice.

'I understand Ghislaine's got a business going, selling executive gifts,' I said.

'You understand right,' said R.M., who was a singularly poor conversationalist that day.

When he had finished eating, he wolf-whistled again for Genius.

'Have you ever read a story by M.R. James called *Oh whistle to me and I'll come to you, my lad*?' I asked.

'No,' said R.M.

By this time, Genius had arrived at the table.

'Will you get the pilot out of the house and bring him here.'

'Yes, Mr Maxwell.'

Genius hurried to the house where he found the pilot, who came to the table.

'I'm leaving now,' said R.M. This was clearly one of his Mr Rochester days.

I got up and kissed him goodbye and he uttered an extraordinary Freudian slip. 'Good luck with your buck!' he said and was helped into the helicopter by the pilot. The ear-splitting blades started whirring and the next minute it was in the sky.

Good God! thought I. The man's even more eccentric than I am!

* * *

In June 1988, R.M. celebrated his 65th birthday. He had three parties, one on 10th June which was his actual birthday, another on 11th June and yet another on 12th June.

The one on 11 June appeared to me to be the most pleasant since it took place in the middle of the day. I had not received an invitation so I just turned up. I knew R.M. used to do that and I was sure he'd be pleased to see me.

It was a very cold day for the time of year so I wore white, tight-fitting, leather trousers, a white V-necked sweater and R.M.'s favourite red snake-skin, stiletto-heeled boots over the trousers. I had on matching red earrings and jewellery. My hair had just been done and I had also had a facial.

The guard, who knew me, stopped me at the gate. I leant out of the car.

'Hullo there. Long time no see. I'm Eleanor Berry and I've lost my invitation card, blast it. How are you keeping?'

The guard let me in.

The lawns were covered with a marquee. I went inside and saw a buffet and tables at which people, whose faces I didn't recognize, guzzled. A cinema screen showed a film about R.M. and his achievements. I got very excited and started to drink. Later, I found Jean Baddeley. A *Mirror* photographer took pictures of her

The village of Solotvino in the Carpathian Mountains. It was here that R.M. was born on 10th June 1923. His original name was Hoch.

R.M.'s family in 1925. He was born under the name of Ludvik Hoch, a.k.a. Abraham Lajbi Hoch. Back row: third from left, his grandfather, Yankel Slomowitz. Fourth from left, his sister Gisl, fifth from left his father, Mehel Hoch. Middle row: Second from left, his grandmother (married to Yankel Slomowitz) third from left, the mother on whom he doted, Hannah Hoch (note her look of extreme serenity). Bottom row: fifth from left, his sister, Brana, fourth from left, R.M. himself. The author does not know the names of the other three boys in the front row on the left.

The suave, sexy, fearless Lieutenant,
cigarette in hand, leading his men in
spring, 1945.

R.M. and his wife Betty, on their wedding
day in Paris on 14th March, 1945.

R.M.'s favourite picture of his wife Betty.
While in valiant service, he kept it with him
everywhere he went, and never tired of
looking at it.

R.M. being awarded the Military Cross by Field-Marshal Montgomery, for his matchless, glorious heroism on the battlefield.

R.M. and Betty with their twin daughters, Isabel and Christine, aged two weeks. Isabel once stated that the author's books were 'very macabre' but the author was amused by the remark.

R.M. recovering from the removal of his left lung, making lightweight of his illness by playing cards with other patients.

Harold Wilson, then Prime Minister, R.M. (centre) and the Mayor of Bletchley (1965).
R.M. was then Labour M.P. for Buckingham.

R.M.'s wife, Betty in later years,
resplendent as ever. The author is still in
touch with her and confides in her her
innermost secrets. Unlike the author,
Betty is, and always will be, a saint.

R.M. in his early days as an M.P.

R.M. canvassing in Buckingham in 1974. He lost the seat and was ill with melancholia for some weeks afterwards.

R.M. and the author.

R.M. giving a book to Leonid Brezhnev in Moscow (1978). Unfortunately, the title of the book and the name of its author were not disclosed. Perhaps a hung-over reporter was covering the event.

The Maxwell family in
1981.
Back row: (from left)
Anne, R.M., Ghislaine,
Isabel, Kevin.
Front row: Christine, Ian,
Betty (after gaining her
D.Phil degree) and
Philip.

A momentous event in the
history of the newspaper
industry. R.M. buys the
Mirror Group papers and
looks like a Saudi
woman, allowed only to
show her eyes.

R.M. in attractive but
sombre pose. Note, he
was left-handed.

R.M. and Betty.

The author's favourite photograph of R.M. It is the first thing she sees by her bed when she wakes up in the morning.

10th June 1988. R.M.'s birthday celebrations at Headington Hill Hall, Oxford.

The Lady Ghislaine. The beautiful white vessel to which the Reaper came, to take its owner's soul.

R.M. is finally laid to rest. May his stormy soul find peace.

Gogol's words are more appropriate than the author's, in relation to this evil spectacle.

'How much inhumanity there is in man, how much savage brutality lies under refined, cultured politeness. . .'

Cover reproduced by kind permission of *Private Eye*; Photo courtesy of PA Photos.

and me standing together.

'Have you seen Bob recently?' I asked.

'Not recently. He's been moving all over the place.'

I went round asking the eaters questions. The alcohol had made me manic.

'He came through here ten minutes ago,' said a woman.

'Then where did he go?' I said, clutching her arm. The expression on her face was identical to that of the wedding guest's when pestered by the Ancient Mariner.

'Where is he? Where is he? You've got to take me to him – now!'

'I can't. I've never met him.'

'You mean you don't know him? Why are you here then?'

'My name was taken from the telephone directory, I suppose.'

'What the hell are you talking about? Do you think I'm going to believe that?'

I moved on to another table and harassed its occupants in a similar manner; then I saw one of the Maxwell twins, leading a tiny child by the hand.

'Christine!' I shouted.

'No. It's Isabel.'

'Sorry about that.' I peered piercingly into her eyes. 'Isabel, you *must* take me to your father. Where is he?'

'He's in the house. By the way, I liked your *Rex Malone* even though it was terribly macabre.'

'Come on, it wasn't particularly macabre. Never mind the book! Please come with me to your father.'

'All right, calm down. Whatever's the matter?'

'Nothing. I just want to be taken to your father.'

'I'm going to see him myself. We'll go together.'

I couldn't keep up with Isabel because my stiletto heels kept sticking in the grass. She waited for me. Then she took me to her father. Her small son, Alexander, had painted the cover of a picture book. It was a gift for R.M.

R.M. was standing in an inner chamber. I didn't know which room it was because its ceiling and walls were draped with white cloth like an Arab's tent.

'Hullo, Bob. Happy birthday,' I said and kissed him.

As always, he was pleased to see me. He introduced me to men of his age.

'This is Eleanore Berry and I'm one of her greatest admirers,' he told the people with him. 'When she was very young, she joined the Communist Party and went to Russia alone, having taught herself to speak Russian like a bloody native. She's got guts.'

He was unusually talkative that day because he was happy. He added: 'She's got a hell of a lot of stories to tell you about her adventures. Once, she worked in a mortuary. After that, she got a job as a bloody nanny and lasted for ten minutes.'

There was muffled laughter. R.M. turned to the boy who gave him the picture book. The cover was worded in a childlike hand, probably helped by an adult 'To Grandad who lives in a helicopter all day'.

R.M. laughed and picked the small boy up. A black cloud descended on me because I had lost his attention.

Isabel helped herself to crudités and passed them to me.

'Why did your nanny job only last for ten minutes?' asked R.M.

'I don't know. I went to the house and found the children's mother in the kitchen. I introduced myself. "Would you bring your children into the kitchen, please," I said.

'She called them, giving me a curious look. Three teenaged boys, who didn't need a nanny, came to the kitchen.

' "Line up against the wall in order of size," I said. "What are your names?"

They gave their names which I forgot.

' "Go and get your ball. Then we can have a game on the lawn and I can get to know you better."

' "I'm afraid your services are no longer required," said their mother as if I had sexually assaulted them.

' "Why are my services no longer required? You haven't sampled them yet. Your attitude is disgraceful," I said.

' "I would like you to leave my house, now," she replied.

' "Don't worry, lady, I shall. Besides, your children are far too big to need a nanny, unless they are mentally retarded." '

Isabel laughed. 'Ellie, you're quite mad!' she said.

R.M. started talking to me in Russian and it was fortunate that I had been brushing up the language for a month in anticipation of this occasion. We had a short conversation in Russian and I said I could only speak it perfectly if I was drunk.

I waited for him to roar with laughter, which he did and I laughed with him. None of the other people in the room, including Isabel and her son, spoke Russian. Once again, I felt a surge of

90

elation. The speaking of Russian seemed to strengthen my bond with R.M.

I was determined to sit at R.M.'s table and went into the kitchen to talk to Betty. Lunch consisted of caviare, lobster, cold chicken in a sauce, and strawberries.

R.M. poured some vodka into his glass to drink with the caviare.

'May I have some, please?' I said.

'No. I can't give it to you as it will make you ill. You've already had several glasses of wine. Last time you got drunk here, you started talking to me about necrophilia.'

'Oh, please, Bob. Go on. Be a sport.'

'No. I categorically forbid it. You'll be ill.'

The Speed I had taken was beginning to wear off. I threw my napkin under the table to give the impression I had dropped it and took more Speed.

When I got up, I noticed a Polish woman sitting next to R.M. She was slim, her long curly blonde hair was dishevelled and she wore a see-through white garment descending into her cleavage. Her skirt was strategically raised and her sun-tanned legs were crossed and could be seen across the table. She tried to exclude me from the conversation to get as much of R.M.'s attention as she could, speaking Polish.

I wasn't going to have any of this and gave her a homicidal glare. I'm sure Betty, too, resented her presence and her brazen behaviour.

R.M. was called to the telephone. Apparently Gorbachev was wishing him happy birthday. I seized the opportunity to speak to the Polish woman when R.M. was out of the room. I caught her eye and said, 'For Christ's sake put your legs under the table and cover them with your skirt. This is a respectable residence, not a disorderly house. And another thing, stop monopolizing Bob's attention!'

When R.M. returned, she talked to him incessantly but I constantly interrupted her.

'Bob, may I have a signed copy of Joe Haines's biography of you? It could be a late birthday present.'

'Yes, of course you can. I'll have it sent to you. When was your birthday?'

'A month ago.'

'What date?'

'May 6th.'

Thereafter, R.M. addressed everyone about his experiences during the war. I revelled in his heroic exploits and stared at him throughout, hoping to catch his eye.

When lunch was over, I went to the marquee and watched another film about R.M.'s achievements before going home. That was one of the happiest days of my life.

Within a week, I received the book. R.M. had even remembered when my birthday was. He had written in the book: 'To Eleanor, from Bob, in friendship.' I display the book at home, together with some of R.M.'s other presents to me. I had just come back from a friend's funeral when the book reached me. It cheered me up for the rest of the day.

I stayed at Headington Hill Hall again soon after but R.M. wasn't there. When I came down the drive, I never looked at the pillars outside the house where he left his car, just in case the space was empty, meaning he was away.

I got out with my suitcase and rang the bell, in low spirits because there was no car outside. Genius opened the door.

'Good evening. Is Mr Maxwell not at home?'

'No, Miss.'

'Do you know if he will be coming home tomorrow?'

'I don't know.'

'Is he ill?'

'I don't know anything about him, Miss.'

'Oh, I thought you worked for him.'

'Sometimes.'

'Where is he?'

'He could be anywhere, Miss.'

Then I understood that this man wasn't called 'Genius' for nothing.

'Mrs Maxwell's here, Miss,' he said. 'May I take your suitcase?'

'Thank you.'

I went in and the first thing I wanted was a stiff gin and tonic.

I found R.M.'s nephew and niece sitting in the drawing room. They were the children of R.M.'s charming and friendly sister, Sylvia Rosen. Sylvia's son, whose name I can't remember, was about eight foot tall which is why R.M. always referred to him as 'the dwarf'.

He had a nickname for most of the people he knew. When he was an M.P., one of his employees was called 'Mr Mutton'.

92

Mutton rang him up one day. 'B-a-a-ah!' shouted R.M. when he lifted the receiver. He called the charming Oping, his Filipino cook, 'Opium'. He referred to my paternal aunt, Sheila Birkenhead, as 'the old Banbury aunt'. I could give countless other examples of his engaging, child-like wit.

'Where's your uncle?' I asked his niece. 'Why isn't he here?'

'Don't ask me. I haven't the faintest idea where he is. I saw Ghislaine yesterday. She had a cold.'

I regarded this as unsolicited information.

I went to the bar and poured myself a gin and tonic. I drank it in one go and a few minutes later, I felt more relaxed. Eventually, Betty came downstairs and I greeted her and gave her a box of chocolates for the house.

'Is Bob not well?' I asked calmly.

'Bob's not at all well. Unfortunately, he's had to stay at the *Mirror*. He's got very bad toothache and we're trying to get hold of a dentist.'

'Oh, dear! Am I allowed to smoke a cigarette in here?'

'*Mais non!*' I was told emphatically.

'I know a dentist called Russell King in Cavendish Square.' I quoted the phone number. 'But I'm not sure whether he practises at weekends.'

'Oh dear, oh dear!'

'What about ringing Talking Pages? They have a list of dentists which states whether they work at weekends. I'll ring them if you like.'

'That's very sweet of you. At the moment I could do with a drink. What will you have?'

'Perrier and ice, please.' (The gin was getting to my head.)

'I can see you live dangerously! Won't you have something stronger?'

'I won't, thanks.'

Genius came in to say dinner was ready. By the time I'd had a few glasses of wine, I felt better.

'Are you writing another book?' asked Betty.

'Not yet,' I said. 'I've been in deadlock for two years.'

'Oh, you lazy old thing!'

The rest of the conversation took place between her and myself. The niece and nephew were subdued and silent.

Later, Betty took me down to the wine cellar. The walls on the stairs leading to the cellar were covered with photographs of R.M., including the heroic picture of Field Marshal Montgomery attaching the MC to his chest for his bravery in the field. This is a powerfully moving picture and I have a replica of it on my bedroom wall, together with other pictures of R.M. which, since his death, have cheered and comforted me.

There was another picture on the cellar stairs. R.M. was standing on a bridge, wearing a beige overcoat, looking lovingly at the camera.

'That's beautiful,' I said. 'How I wish it were mine!'

Betty hurriedly took it down and placed it in my hands. I was mortified with embarrassment and shame.

'I can't possibly take this picture away from you. It would be terribly wrong.'

She was determined to give it to me and in return I wrote her a long letter of appreciation.

In the cellar was a large cabinet near the bottles of wine. Betty got out a towering pile of photographs, mostly of her husband. She very kindly gave me all the photographs I found attractive, including one of me standing with Bob. She had taken the photograph herself.

When we'd finished in the cellar, she took me to her study and showed me some leather-bound volumes full of press cuttings. They went back to the days when publicity about him had started.

I thought what a rare and saintly lady she was and was moved by the trouble she took to show me all these things until 1.00 o'clock in the morning, when she must have been exhausted. I felt at one with her, and R.M.'s absence no longer troubled me. It was as if he were in the house.

I didn't sleep that night so I dressed and went down to breakfast in the kitchen at 8.30. Betty came down later and I got up and greeted her. She addressed me in French but my French had suffered appallingly because of the insomnia I had had the night before.

'How about all those dentists, Betty?'

'How kind of you to ask! I managed to get a dentist lined up late last night. Bob's seeing him this morning.'

I said I was relieved. Genius brought me some fresh orange juice and gave a pile of newspapers to Betty. We sat and ate and read.

Later, I helped her wrap up Christmas presents and put a colossal pile of cards into envelopes. They appeared to be addressed to each citizen in every country in the world, including myself and my father.

'Oh, I'll take those, Betty, there's no point in sending them out.'

This year's card was fairly low profile, showing the words Pergamon Press in gold letters against a blue background. Whenever I stayed with the Maxwells just before Christmas, I always took the cards for my father and myself.

I learnt something through disagreeable experience. Every Christmas, guests came to our house. If R.M. had his own picture on his card and it was unflattering, guests would take it down and pass it round the room, joking about it.

'Look here, we're not having any Maxwell jokes in this house!' said my loyal father angrily.

Another guest took the card down the following year.

'Why does that man send his photograph out?' she said, unfortunately in my hearing.

I went up to her menacingly with a glass of neat whisky in my hand. I stood over her, glaring at her. I drained the glass before addressing her.

'What did you say?' I shouted.

Fear came into her voice and her face.

'I only asked why that man had to send his photograph out,' she said, very timidly.

'I'll tell you why! Because the person you call "that man", whose picture you took from my father's mantelpiece to comment on it, has done nothing but heroic deeds all his life, as well as saving my life. If you had done what he did, *you* would probably send pictures of yourself out.'

I was taught a lesson. Every time I went to the Maxwells before Christmas, I destroyed the card to my father and whenever he asked where it was, I explained that Betty was under too much pressure and would not be sending any cards out.

* * *

I rang R.M.'s office at the *Mirror* and asked if I could go round there to see him. He had often asked me to make a date to visit him. One of his many secretaries, Andrea Martin, took my call. I later saw a photograph of both of them barefoot walking on a beach towards the sunset. This caused me agonising jealousy. I later learnt that R.M. had fallen for this woman in a major way. It could have been proper love, or blind infatuation. Nick Davies, the *Mirror* journalist, about whom I shall say more later on, was in love with her and is now married to her. I know R.M. suffered the tortures of the damned when he realized she was having an affair with Davies. He called his rival into his office and became exceptionally emotional. He made choking noises and could hardly speak, except when drinking a glass of water. I believe Andrea's marriage broke his heart. He was never well again after this event.

'Is it possible for Mrs Maxwell to be there too? I haven't seen her for a long time either,' I said to Andrea.

'What do you want to speak to Mr and Mrs Maxwell about?' asked Andrea.

'Oh, just my usual interests, homosexual sado-porn, black rubber mackintoshes, whips, the Marquis de Sade, drugs, street-fights, necrophilia, flick-knives, that sort of thing.'

'Are you serious? What *do* you really want to talk to Mr Maxwell about?'

'I'm sure Mr Maxwell will tell you afterwards if he thinks you need to know. Would you please look for a free date in his diary without asking me any further questions. I hope I haven't offended you by speaking plainly.'

Andrea's tone became less brisk and more genial.

She named a date: 'He's free then but only for a drink. Last time you rang, you said you'd like to see the *Mirror* come off the presses. He'd like to show you but he has to go out afterwards.'

'That sounds fine.'

'Mrs Maxwell will be coming to the *Mirror* that evening so you may easily see her too,' said Andrea.

I slept badly every night until I was due to go to the *Mirror*. I bought R.M. some caviare and some flowers for Betty. That day, I couldn't concentrate on my work at all. I went out to lunch but had no appetite. When I came back, I spent my time pacing up and down. Later that afternoon, I had to take 20 mg of Valium. I left my office, forgetting to turn off the computer, and as I wasn't due to see R.M. at the *Mirror* until later on, I went to the pub and got slightly drunk, smoked forty cigarettes and read James Hadley Chase. I drank because I was afraid of going into the *Mirror* building and not being able to find him there.

The smell of whisky was on my breath but I knew from previous occasions that R.M. never expressed disapproval of that unless the drinker happened to be working for him.

When I thought I was able to walk, I continued my journey to my destination. It seemed like 300 miles because my snake-skin boots (R.M.'s favourites) were agony. I had on a pale green leather suit to please him.

I couldn't make the walk and got a taxi for the rest of the journey. I was jumpy and unpleasantly edgy throughout the ride. The driver was pretty bad-tempered as well. We had a row about the shortness of the journey, and I got out refusing to pay him.

I was still early for R.M. I went to a pub just opposite Maxwell House in Fetter Lane. I swallowed a few Speed and continued to read James Hadley Chase. Then I entered the building with a feeling of monumental euphoria.

'I'm here to see Mr Maxwell,' I said to a guard behind a desk. He made a call to certify my presence was genuine and took me to the lift.

The ground floor looked immaculately clean but very ordinary. The lift ascended to the top floor. When it opened, I saw an entirely new world.

I am not an authority on interior decoration but the room I had been left in looked majestic and was adorned with seventeenth- and eighteenth-century paintings. The furniture might have belonged to kings and the carpets were embroidered with the letter M. With what I had consumed and taken, I felt like Dante ascending to the firmament to be re-united with Beatrice.

There was no one there to greet me but I didn't care. A huge window, covering a wall, showed a panoramic view of London. I had an urge to smoke but couldn't because R.M. and Betty were averse to anyone smoking in front of them. This may have been due to R.M.'s diseased lung when he was in his 30s.

I grew restless and started walking round in circles. Eventually, I came to a chess set with intricately carved pieces. A game was in progress. I moved the pieces back to their original places and started a game with myself, walking backwards and forwards, quietly whistling 'A Silent Crowd Gathered Outside of Kilmainham'.

A servant suddenly entered the room.

'You shouldn't have moved those men,' he said in an anxious

voice. 'You have interrupted a game between Mr Maxwell and the Russian Ambassador.'

'Oh, dearie me!'

'Perhaps you would care for a drink?'

'Yes, please. I'll have a double whisky if that's all right with you. Where's Mr Maxwell? He is here, isn't he?'

'Yes, he is here,' said the servant. 'He's expecting you but he's still in his office. I really would thank you not to touch his chessmen. He's very proud of them.'

'I won't touch them, Scout's honour,' I said.

Eventually Betty came in, splendidly attired. She explained she had to go out to dinner.

We had a long talk about the lives of each of her children whom she said were all very happy, with the exception of one. She talked at length about R.M. whom she said was working too hard and causing her concern.

'But with Bob, work is play,' I said. 'When he works, he's like a child playing with his toys. Surely it must be good for him. If he stopped, he'd go off his head.'

'I hope you're right. Ghislaine bought a beautiful dress in Paris last week.' She described the dress at length.

'You are all right, aren't you?' she asked. It's possible I was fidgety and uncoordinated, due to the alcohol and Speed.

'Yes. Has Ghislaine got another man? Oh sorry, that was none of my business!'

'She's been going out with the same man for some time now.' She gave his name which was of such incredible length, it would have covered the front page of a tabloid newspaper.

'Does Bob like him?'

'No. There's a big problem there. He can't stand him.'

'Do you know why?'

'He's Italian and Bob has a pathological loathing for Italians.'

'Why doesn't he like Italians?'

'I don't really know. Part of it is that he thinks they're all drunken idiots.'

We talked for a few more minutes until she said she had to go. I gave her the flowers I had bought for her.

'You won't have to wait much longer now. One of the secretaries will take you in to Mr Maxwell as soon as he's ready,' said another of R.M.'s employees, on coming into the room. I had no idea what his name was. He failed to introduce himself.

I knew the heinous consequences of smoking in front of R.M. A woman ushered me into a lavish hallway with magenta velvet chairs, where she said I could smoke, provided I put the cigarette out as soon as R.M. came out of his office. I didn't want him to catch me so I had a cigarette in his private lavatory. Andrea Martin was outside in the corridor.

'You had a cigarette in Mr Maxwell's lavatory,' she said, confrontationally. 'Mr Maxwell knows you had a cigarette in his lavatory.'

R.M. never mentioned the matter to me. That was what was so nice about him.

My heart was going frighteningly fast because of the Speed – so much so that I could hear it. There were quite a few boring-looking women up there, all dressed in pretty boring-looking uniforms. I asked one of the women to give me a copy of the *Mirror* and started doing the crossword.

In ten minutes, R.M. came out and kissed me on the mouth. He took me into his American-style office and I was surprised to see he had all the blinds drawn and the lights out, except for a small Anglepoise lamp on his desk.

'You're looking more beautiful by the minute,' he said. 'I like the sexy leather.'

I said nothing. I smiled radiantly and rolled my eyes at him.

'I've brought you some of your favourite *Beluga*,' I said. He was pleased and he gave me another kiss, this time on the forehead.

'May I open my present now?' he asked. The loveable, child-like question enchanted me.

'Yes, of course. You should taste it, to make sure it's the one you want.'

'There's something worrying you, isn't there?' he said suddenly. 'Come on, let's have it.'

I had an obsession about one of the women who worked with me. I hated her guts at the time and lay awake at night thinking of ways to kill her, although I got on well with her later on.

Her name was Nicola Gibbon. I had been at the hospital for three years and was highly regarded. Nicola Gibbon, on the other hand, was only an agency temp. The Administrator, a rugger-playing Welshman, called us all in without warning and told us that Nicola was being promoted over my head. A woman called Doris Nicholson was my best friend at the hospital. We had lunch together every day and I would tell her about my fantasy of murdering Nicola.

Unfortunately, Nicola Gibbon had information about me, which I did not wish known. If I'd finished my work, I sometimes went to the cinema in the afternoons. She found out. She had a loud, carrying voice and an East End accent. She was talking to some people in the front office. 'I 'erd she goes to the pictures some afternoons. I tell a lie. Sometimes, she 'as 'er 'air done.'

I told R.M. the whole story.

He leant his head on one side and raised his eyebrows, as if to say 'you bloody fool!'

'Why on earth did you allow Nicola Gibbon to do that?' he said.

'It was all done behind my back, blast it! It was engineered behind closed doors like a *coup*.'

R.M. chewed on his unlit cigar.

'And what is our Eleanore going to do to get rid of Piccolo Lipkin?'

'Nicola Gibbon,' I corrected. 'There's nothing I can do at this stage but if she hots up, I'll call the Branch Secretary of NALGO in.'

R.M. swivelled on his chair.

'I have an important proposition to make to you.'

'What would that be?'

'Chuck Lipkin altogether.'

'Gibbon.'

'Gibbon, Lipkin, call her what you will! Do you know what I'm trying to say to you?'

'As a matter of fact, no.'

'I'm asking you if you'd like to come and work for me at the *Mirror*. When I offered you a job twenty years ago, you turned me down. Perhaps this time, you'll say yes.'

I had a yearning for a cigarette and was just about to get one out but checked myself.

'I'm so sorry but I'll have to turn your offer down. I'm afraid I will only work in hospitals. I like the hustle and bustle of bestethoscoped, white-coated men rushing down corridors and the toing and froing of stretchers borne by sweating porters. I like the smells in hospitals. They remind me of my school.'

R.M. looked aghast.

'You can't fool me,' he said jocularly. 'I've known you since you

100

were little more than a puppy. You like the stench of death and decay. You love the blood and guts. Don't think I don't know about all this. I read that extraordinary book you wrote about me, remember?'*

I was slightly embarrassed. I wanted a cigarette. I looked around the room, still curious as to why the blinds were drawn and the lights turned off.

'I'll tell you what, Bob. I will work for you on one condition and one condition only.'

'Which is what, sweetie?'

'That you train to become a doctor and later a consultant surgeon, wearing a dazzling white coat in plush rooms in Harley Street, and having an array of swivelling, leather-studded chairs and a swish leather-studded couch.'

'Christ, you're barmy! Come with me and I'll show you the *Mirror*.'

When we got outside the dark room, I noticed R.M. much more fully in the glaring lights from the ceiling.

I had no idea he was dying of emphysema and impairment of oxygen to the brain. Nor did I know that in only a few months, his thinking processes would deteriorate to such a terrifying degree that no one would dare go near him. Every time I rang his office during the last months of his life, excuses were made that he was living in America. I also had no idea that this was the last time I would see him.

I observed him closely under the glaring light. I had never seen him look so attractive since he was young. He had lost some weight and his thick black hair was slightly dishevelled. The only thing that struck me as strange was the fact that his eyes failed to focus on an object for more than a second at a time. We went up to the office occupied by his editors.

As we entered their office, the editors, who had been lolling, threw themselves into their work. I found the power that their boss held over them devastatingly sexually attractive. The scene was akin to Beatrice showing Dante the firmament. R.M. said what he always did when introducing me. He said I joined the Communist Party,

---

Never Alone with Rex Malone. This book, though funny, is extremely morbid in places. It contains a lot of black humour.

taught myself Russian and went to Russia alone. I was beginning to find these words soporific. The editors looked baffled. I questioned them at length about their previous employment.

'What story are you running?' he asked one of the editors.

'We're covering the actress [sorry, readers, I've forgotten her name] who has become a born-again Christian.'

'A fine story,' said R.M. 'It's never too late to turn to God.'

'Oh, most assuredly, Mr Maxwell!' said the editor.

R.M. had already given me more whisky and I feared I was drunk. I stared at the Napoleonic colossus surrounded by his soldiers and I got a bit out of control.

'Do you cover stories about harassment in hospitals?' I asked one of the editors in a booming voice, two octaves lower than its ordinary pitch.

R.M. put his hand on my shoulder.

'Now, we're not going to discuss that woman, Piccolo Lipkin in here.'

'Nicola Gibbon.'

'Never mind what her bloody name is! Come and meet Mr Whittaker who is our Royal Correspondent.'

I shook Mr Whittaker's hand and smiled. I was feeling sick.

R.M. addressed his editors collectively as they remained standing, reluctant to return to their desks.

'Do you know that I've just offered Eleanore a job on the *Mirror*?'

'Indeed, Mr Maxwell?' said the editor running the story on the born-again Christian.

'And do you know she's turned my offer down a second time, the cheeky monkey.'

'I'm sorry to hear that,' said the editor.

'She prefers to work in hospitals, because she's obsessed by death,' said R.M. 'She only likes to be in places where there's plenty of blood and guts. She hangs about outside mortuaries waiting for hearses to turn up.'

The editor cleared his throat.

I then shook hands again with the editors who maintained their angelic smiles. R.M. took me to see the *Mirror* coming off the presses.

When I recounted this wonderful experience to Nicky and likened the smiling editors to the characters in *Paradiso*, he said I

102

was completely mad.

'Don't you realize they were all terrified of Maxwell?' he said.

When the *Mirror* came off the presses, the machines made an unbroken rhythmic noise as they moved from one level to another. I was hypnotized by them. I saw before me a river of volcanic lava, sent by the gods in colours of red and white, purifying the earth, and the fleece of freshly-shorn lambs and newly-fallen snow. Beside me, stood the velvet black bear, taking me by the hand. A Christian might have likened this to the Second Coming.

I stood engrossed as the wonderful spectacle unfolded before me and as I raised my eyes to the big black bear, I wept.

'Have you got a car?' he asked when he'd shown me the presses.

'No. There's nowhere to park in London.'

'That's no problem. I'll get one of my drivers to take you home.'

'That's very kind of you. Are you sure?'

'Stop saying I'm kind. Yes of course I'm sure.'

A car drew up in the yard. The driver later told me he had driven Ghislaine to represent her father at the funeral of Marjorie Proops's husband.

R.M. kissed me goodbye. It is horrifying to think that I had no idea I would never see him again.

'Goodbye, Missy and thank you for my prezzie. Do try and get away from all this blood and guts, and stop hanging around outside mortuaries.'

'I'll try, Bob. Thank you so much for taking the time to show me round the *Mirror*.'

* * *

Amidst my tragic tale, I have a comical story to tell regarding Marjorie Proops.

After R.M.'s death, there was prurient speculation about women going to bed with him; sometimes I saw it in the press, sometimes on the television. I also read that R.M. had frequently addressed Mrs Proops as 'My darling little daughter'.

I couldn't really imagine R.M. taking this woman to his bed but my obsession was such that I was prepared to believe anything. One morning, after pacing up and down the room, a demon got into me and made me ring Mrs Proops at the *Mirror*.

'Mrs Proops. You've got to help me. I'm possessed. I wrote to

103

you several times but got no reply [a lie]. Please, you've got to help me,' I repeated.

Mrs Proops's voice was quite plummy. Her brogue could have been one of many London accents. She answered but her tone was unfriendly. I came straight out with it.

'Mrs Proops – I must know – when Robert Maxwell kissed you, was it on the cheek or on the mouth?'

'I find you most impertinent. Who are you?'

'My name's Natalie Klein [the heroine in *Never Alone with Rex Malone*]. I'm not being rude but I *must* know.'

'You *are* being rude, blooming rude. What exactly do you want? Robert Maxwell was a very affectionate man.'

'When you say he was an "affectionate man", does that mean he used to beckon you into dark corners and put his hand between your legs?'

Mrs Proops hung up.

7

It was beginning to get dark on the afternoon of Tuesday, 5th November, 1991. Rita Cassidy, my Irish colleague, and I were in our office at the hospital, busy with our computers. Rita was quite a fiery woman in her thirties. I had a love–hate relationship with her although we were good friends some of the time.

We were taking a break. I was in a good mood and rolled up balls of paper and flicked them towards her. In retaliation she sang 'Blowing in the Wind' which she knew I hated. I feel a sense of foreboding whenever I hear it.

'For Christ's sake, stop singing that horrible morbid song!' I shouted. 'Its eerie. It makes me feel that something not quite right's going on out there.'

The telephone rang.

'Answer that,' I said, 'as a penalty for singing that song!'

'It's your turn to answer.'

'Answer that phone!' I said peremptorily.

A voice on the other end of the line asked to speak to me. The caller was my brother, Adrian. I took the call.

'Hullo.' I could tell by the tone of his voice that he was bringing me bad news.

'Is everything all right?' I said, thinking illogically that such words would put right whatever he was going to tell me.

'No. I'm afraid I have some rather startling news for you.'

'Has someone in the family had an accident? Is someone ill?' I shouted.

This was inconveniencing Rita who wanted to get her work finished in time to go to a fireworks party with her man. I thought this was a funny form of celebration for an Irish woman to attend.

'I'm afraid it's about Robert Maxwell,' said Adrian. 'I'm telling you now, before you go out and see it on the news-stands.'

My immediate reaction was of relief that no one in my family had been hurt but my hysteria mounted quickly on fearing that harm had come to R.M.

'Bob? Is he still alive?' I shouted.

'I'm afraid he's gone missing.'

'Gone missing? Gone missing? Missing from what?'

'The news has just come in from Reuters. He was on his boat, the *Lady Ghislaine*, and went to bed last night. He must have got up during the night and gone out on to the deck. This morning, a search party was sent out when he wasn't in his room and he wasn't anywhere to be found. He must either have accidentally fallen from the boat into the sea, or committed suicide. He was in severe debt. That could be a motive for suicide.'

'Of course he couldn't have fallen into the sea,' I said. 'Nor could he possibly have taken his life. The man would never ever have taken his life. It wouldn't be his style. The boat is very big.' I was saying this to console myself rather than to accept reality. 'Just because someone can't be found, it doesn't mean they're not there.'

I could tell by my brother's voice that my efforts not to accept the truth were distressing him, because he was certain R.M. had drowned during the night, and he felt it was his responsibility to tell me.

'Even all the lavatories have been searched.'

'But it would take hours to search all the lavatories. I should imagine there are about eighteen lavatories on that boat! Besides, if one of the lavatories were locked, no crew-member would dare to bang on the door, to see if the Captain was on the other side of it.'

'No,' said my brother, 'every lavatory has been searched. I'm afraid he's been drowned.'

'How could he have done that by accident? He was murdered!' I shouted.

I felt faint. I was alerted by the sound of Rita shouting at Adrian. She had snatched the receiver from me.

'Why are you shouting?' I demanded. She continued to shout at Adrian.

'You should never have rung your sister up! You should have come here and told her face to face! You're very irresponsible.'

'Don't speak to my brother like that,' I said.

I took the receiver.

'Why don't you get a taxi to my office?'

'Is there any whisky there?' I asked urgently.

'Yes, yes, plenty of whisky. Come on over.'

Rita had to go and watch the fireworks so she rang Doris and told her the sad news. Doris, forever faithful, came up immediately.

Some of the doctors were coming into the office to check patients' results before prescribing antibiotics. One of the Senior House Officers,* Melanie Shaw, was supportive and held my hand. Doris told her what had happened.

'I think I need to get out of here,' I said.

Doris and Melanie helped me outside.

'You'll get a taxi, won't you?' said Melanie.

'No. Doris and I are going out for a drink. Would you like to come with us?'

'I can't,' said Melanie. 'I've got to get back to the ward to see patients.'

'Thank you so much for helping me down,' I said, 'I won't forget this.'

Doris bought me a considerable amount of whisky in the Red Lion across the road. The whisky released the grief. I began to cry while a nice man at the bar kindly, if somewhat unwisely, bought me even more. It was the actor, Bob Hoskins. Readers of the *Evening Standard* quietly read their papers, sometimes rattling them in the air to get to the inner pages. The headlines kept flashing in front of my eyes, lashing them with acid.

The most unpleasant thing of all was the spirit of jubilation with which these people read the news.

MAXWELL IS DEAD;
MAXWELL DIES AT SEA;
MAXWELL IS DROWNED.

* * *

There had been a lot of serious confusion at home, due to the crass stupidity of the afternoon caretaker whose name was Joe. I rang him up from the Red Lion and told him to tell my man friend, whom I shall refer to as H, that R.M. had been drowned. I didn't want to have to tell him myself.

---

*Senior House Office (SHO): Euphemism for a junior doctor in an NHS hospital.

I also told him about Doris's husband. He is a singularly eccentric man, who dresses like a skiing instructor. He was known as 'Napoleon' because of his uncanny resemblance to the Emperor. I told the caretaker he would be going to the flat long before Doris and I returned, and I told him to let Napoleon in.

When I made this call in the crowded pub with Doris at my side, I had already had too much to drink and I was hysterical but by no means incoherent. I did not realize how loudly I was shouting but Doris told me later that I had reduced the room to silence.

I rang Headington Hill Hall (calmly) to tell Betty how deeply shocked and horrified I was. Her secretary, Jay Miller, told me in a shaking voice that Betty and Philip (her eldest surviving son) had already flown to Tenerife to identify R.M. Then I ran out of coins.

When I rang the caretaker of the building he refused to accept the charge. I rang him three or four times, giving my surname with which he was unfamiliar. He still refused. If I'd had a gun, I probably would have gone round and shot him.

Doris got some change from the flabbergasted barman. 'She's talking to a man who's deaf and she's been cut off,' she said adroitly.

I rang the caretaker and asked him what he meant by refusing to accept my calls.

'Listen very carefully,' I shouted. 'If you can't remember what I say, write it down.'

'Yes, Miss Berry.'

'Two things: First, Robert Maxwell has been drowned. Have you understood that and written it down?'

'Who's Robert Maxwell?' asked the half-witted man. 'Is he a resident here?'

'No. You will find a man in my flat to whom you will break the news I have just given you. Just repeat my words.'

'I'm to go and find a man upstairs and tell him Michael Jackson has been run over.'

The man was one of these proverbial walking dickheads. I had to repeat myself several times.

'There's a second thing. A man calling himself Napoleon, who dresses like a skiing instructor, will be coming to this address shortly. Please let him in and send him upstairs. Repeat these two messages, please.'

The caretaker appeared more confused than ever. Yes, my

instructions were confusing, but would not have been, had he written them down.

'A man was drowned and another man will be collecting Napoleon for his skiing lesson,' he said.

My spirit had been broken by the caretaker's calculated obtuseness. The barman came over to Doris and asked her to take me outside. He said I was making too much noise and that I was never to go on the premises again.

Doris and I took a taxi home. The whisky had made me manic. I started to sing 'For Those in Peril on the Sea' followed by 'The Wearing of the Green'. The manic attack was infectious. Doris started singing as well. The taxi driver covered his ears whenever he could and closed the internal window.

I let myself and Doris into the flat where H. and Napoleon were waiting. I can't remember a thing about this small gathering except for the fact that Napoleon was eating large quantities of biscuits. It was like a dream. Napoleon and Doris left after about half an hour. I then told H. about the tragedy as the half-witted caretaker had failed to pass on the message.

I can't remember what happened after that. All I remember is that I suffered an injury. H. rang 999 and I was ambulanced off to the Westminster Hospital, and thence to the Charing Cross Hospital.

My friend, Elisa Segrave, who is an extremely talented writer, was in the Charing Cross Hospital at the same time I was in there. I didn't know at the time that she would be writing a book, describing her illness and the patients she met during her stay.

She is the author of *Diary of a Breast*, a witty, page-turning book, written arrestingly in the present tense. She has changed the names of her characters, being obviously fastidious about libel writs. I am represented by a raving mad, drunken woman called Joan, who makes abusive telephone calls to newspapers, shouts about her fear that she will be unable to go to Jerusalem to attend Robert Maxwell's funeral, and uses such unbelievably filthy language that some of her words are unknown even to me. I found the passage hilarious. Elisa has sold a colossal number of copies of *Diary of a Breast*, which I understand has been translated into foreign languages. She is now working on other books and I think she has become a bestseller.

I refused to have a general anaesthetic because I feel ill afterwards. I also like to talk to the surgeons and listen to their fascinating medical jargon and black-humoured jokes. During the operation, I talked at length about my books.

'Miss Berry,' said the Consultant sharply, 'if you say one more word about the contents of your books, you are going to lose your arm.'

After the operation, I was taken to a ward which I shared with three other women. It was bed-time and the Ward Sister was handing out sleeping pills. She passed them from one patient to another in a plastic cup. She came to me last.

'What is this drug?' I asked. It was a small yellow, egg-shaped capsule.

'Temazepam.'

'I'm very sorry but Temazepam belongs to the Benzodiazepine family. It is addictive. When my GP, Dr Ratner came to see one of the nurses here earlier, he gave her instructions for me to take the sleeping pills he had arranged to have flown in from Paris.'

''Ere! 'Ark at Lady Muck!' shouted a woman of about my age, whose bed was in the nicest part of the ward by the window, with a spectacular view of London.

I ignored her. I was more preoccupied with getting the sleeping pills I wanted.

'It's Temazepam or nothing,' said the nurse.

'In that case, would you please bring the telephone in so that I can ring Dr Ratner?'

'Not a chance, I'm afraid. It's too late at night for telephones to be brought onto the ward.'

'All right,' I said, 'would you please ring him from a telephone outside.'

The nurse lost her temper.

'This is not an amusement arcade. We've got other things to do! You're not the only patient here!'

I didn't like her attitude. I got angry.

'My taxes pay for patients to be treated considerately in hospitals. This comes within your job description, advocating courtesy and flexibility. You could get an official written warning for being uncooperative with patients. I've taken your name from your lapel and I shall report you to the Head of Human Resources.' I gave her Dr Ratner's number.

She had been gone for ten minutes.

'Sorry, there's only an answering service.' That meant she wouldn't get consent for anything from half an hour to three hours. At least she had the courage to face me with this news.

'I can't give you the pills that you apparently arranged to have flown in from Paris. You're not written up for them.'

The words 'written up' uttered to me by nurses in all the hospitals I've been in, provoke me beyond belief. When I hear them, I get into a dreadful bait.

'Have you any idea how I came to be here?' I said. 'Do you realize whose death I am mourning?'

'I don't know and I don't care!' said the nurse. 'Stop showing off!'

'Oh, don't you? I'm mourning one of our major national heroes, a man who, with the help of Sir Winston Churchill, won the war almost single-handed. Field Marshal Montgomery personally attached the MC to his chest. This man brought relief to famines in Third World countries. He gave bread to the starving, hope to the despairing and work to the jobless. Even heads of state rang him day and night for advice before they made decisions of global significance. And I can go on ...' (Looking back on it, I admit that my language was a bit 'O.T.T.'. Also, I forgot to give R.M.'s name, which made my statements even more ridiculous.)

'Oh, please don't,' pleaded the nurse.

By this time, I was laughing nervously.

'If you make any more noise, I shall have to send for the Duty Psychiatrist,' she said.

'I don't need a bloody psychiatrist!' I shouted. 'All I want are the pills which were flown in from Paris.'

' 'Course you needs a bloomin' psychiatrist, Lady Muck,' remarked the disagreeable woman in the bed by the window.

I ignored her and directed my energy towards the nurse.

'I'll make a bargain with you, nurse,' I said, 'If you bring me my pills from Paris, I'll go straight to sleep and be as silent as a sedated ant. If you do not, I shall lie on my back until the sun rises and I shall sing 'The Burning of Father Murphy', so loudly that the noise will reverberate round this hospital and probably all the way down the street.'

'Sorry, you haven't been written up,' was her sole reaction to this threat.

'All right, if that's how you feel, I shall open fire. Stand you in

111

readiness to receive my fire?'

'Ain't she pompous!' Again, it was the mad woman by the window. 'Pompous as well as flippin' barmy!'

Date boxes, bananas, grapes and other objects were pelted in my direction. The war had begun. I lay flat on my back. I started off with 'The Hanging of Kevin Barry' which I sang to the tune of 'Clementine', repeating one of the verses several times over:

> 'Kevin Barry, do not leave me.
> Kevin Barry, do not die.'
> Cried his broken-hearted mother
> When she saw the gibbet high.'

There were angry shouts of 'Belt up! Shut your hole!' accompanied by other expletives. I wished R.M. were there to witness the scene! He had always gone round telling people that I was 'one hell of a feisty woman'. He would have loved it, particularly as I was causing a disturbance in his memory.

I sang another song about an IRA man being caught with bombing equipment. Each verse ended monotonously with the words, 'Ah, me coople of sticks of gelig-i-nite and me old alarum clock'.

I suddenly realized that Nicky (my other brother) had brought me two bottles of claret which I had hidden under the bed. I used one arm and opened one by pushing the cork down into the bottle. I drank plenty of it and as a result became even more manic.

> 'It was at the Harrow that the boys from Wexford
> Showed Bookie's Regiment our men could fight.'

Some hours had passed. The wine helped me sing more loudly. I saw nothing of the nurse. It was 4.00 o'clock in the morning and despite the noise, the other patients had gone to sleep on their Temazepam.

I heard the nurse's voice on the telephone across the corridor. Her tone was curt and crisp.

'Mrs Cullen, will you please come and take your sister away from this hospital.'

The timing of the call must have terrified Harriet. She probably thought I had died from some unknown cause and that she was being asked to identify me. I listened, waiting for the nurse to speak again.

'I'm sorry, Mrs Cullen, but your sister is causing a major breach of the peace and is on the verge of bringing this hospital to a standstill. She is the rowdiest, stubbornest and most difficult patient I have ever had to deal with in my entire nursing career.'

Then she came in to see me.

'I'm afraid we really can't tolerate incidents of this nature in this hospital. Your sister will be collecting you in about 20 minutes.'

'Do you mean you rang her up at 4.00 o'clock in the morning and disturbed her household?'

'I had no choice,' said the nurse.

'You had no choice! You had no choice! You've no business disturbing other people's sleep at this hour of the night. Have you no respect for a person's need to get a decent night's rest? A person who wakes people in the night is a phenomenally selfish person.'

'I must say, you're a fine one to talk! Not only that, you smell of drink,' said the nurse provocatively.

'Yes, I know I do. Robert Maxwell's dead.'

'I didn't know you knew him. I heard it on the news.' The nurse didn't comment. She leant against the wall and filed one of her menacing-looking talons.

Soon, Harriet appeared. I felt guilty for having caused her sleep to be disturbed, but she was very tolerant about it. Had I been her, I would have refused to come. She didn't seem concerned about being woken. Instead, she was terrified I was going to be sick.

'Is my sister going to be sick?' she asked urgently, pinning the traumatized nurse against the wall.

'I don't know, Mrs Cullen,' replied the nurse. 'She's had a lot to drink. Apparently, your brother, Nicholas, brought some bottles in and your sister drank them.'

Harriet, my sister, is a sturdy old soul. Her nerves are good but like all Berrys, including myself, she is prone to occasional outbursts of temper. She never panics in a crisis as I do. There is just one thing that repulses her to the point of hysteria, and that is someone being sick in front of her.

'Be honest with me,' she said as she guided me down the corridor, 'is there any risk that you're going to be sick?'

'No, no.'

'It was naughty of Nicky to bring you all that drink. If you are sick, I'm going to be livid with him and I'm going to take you straight to his house.'

'I'm *not* going to be sick!'

Harriet and her kindly husband, Martin, looked after me for a few days and kept me occupied with visits to the cinema. In the evenings, I played with my nephews, Miguel and Mingo, then aged nine and seven. Harriet was anxious not to let me out of the house.

'Why?' I asked.

'Because in your present state, I wouldn't put it past you to take a taxi round to the offices of the *Sun* newspaper and slit someone's throat with a carving knife. It's the sort of thing you might do once you get in a bait.'

Opposite Harriet's kitchen, across a stretch of grass, is a house shared by a group of men. Their bathroom has a wall-to-wall, uncurtained window.

Harriet keeps cases of claret in her kitchen. I opened a bottle and watched these men. Harriet came in.

'What do you mean by drinking at 9.00 o'clock in the morning, so soon after you had hepatitis? Anyone would think you *want* to get cirrhosis of the liver, like so many of the alcoholics in the Smith and Berry side of the family!'

'I was just coming down to look at the men before breakfast.' As I spoke I caught one of them by the eye and waved.

Harriet was acutely embarrassed.

'Don't do that! I have to *live* here!'

After breakfast, I read the papers. Reading about R.M., before the press turned on him, comforted me.

The next day I had to see Peter Rohde, a psychiatrist up Harley. He's the man on whom Dr Suede, in *Someone's Been Done Up Harley* is modelled. The book is going to be made into a film.

By the time I got to Rohde's consulting rooms, I was inebriated and manic. Instead of going to Rohde's rooms first, I went into the wrong building. I went into a room on the ground floor which was identical, from the outside, to Rohde's consulting room.

The man I faced was bending over a patient but when he saw me he sprang to his feet. He was too startled to ask who I was. In the end it transpired he was a dentist and I was too befuddled to realize this. He was about five foot tall, wore outmoded black-rimmed glasses and was as bald as a billiard ball.

114

'Are you Peter Rohde, the psychiatrist?'

'Do I look like a psychiatrist?'

'You do, a bit.'

A pause ensued while the dentist gathered what wits he could. His patient, a woman with tight black curls, leaned timidly round from her supine chair, her mouth gaping open in amazement.

'Who are you?' the dentist eventually managed to splutter.

I talked incoherently to him about Robert Maxwell.

The dentist looked gobsmacked. His patient continued to gape at me.

'Will you go away, please,' said the dentist, his voice lowered as if breaking tragic news.

Rohde was standing waiting for me in the street. He looked as if he had left his entire family in a burning house.

'Have you harmed anyone, Miss Berry?' he said in a high-pitched voice. (Only a psychiatrist would be likely to ask an extraordinary question like that.)

'No,' I said.

The consulting room used by Rohde was extremely dingy. I could tell that he had borrowed it from another doctor. Books on urology lay on occasional tables. Photographs of a hunt adorned the mantelpiece.

'What actually happened between you and that dentist?' he asked.

'Not a lot. Mistook him for you, didn't I?'

'Is that supposed to be a backhanded compliment?'

'Neither a compliment nor an insult.'

'Did you know he [R.M.] had been ill?'

'How the hell should I know whether the dentist had been ill?'

'No. Did you know Mr Maxwell had been ill?'

At that time, I was unaware that he'd been ill. Betty told me after his death that his remaining lung was being dangerously deprived of oxygen. Interestingly, when Ghislaine was interviewed by a glossy magazine years after her father's death, she denied that he had been ill at all and was adamant that he had been murdered. Surely, she must have realized he was ill. She had been seeing him a great deal, up to the time of his death. Perhaps, she had forced herself into denial, unable to accept that he was dying.

'He was never ill,' I said bitterly. 'He was murdered. Someone pushed him into the water.'

'Tell me about the accident you had,' asked Rohde.

'I don't see the point. It bears no relevance to the case.'

'Oh, doesn't it?'

'I've just told you it doesn't so there's an end to it.'

I was still very intoxicated. I fell over and passed out.

Shortly afterwards, I received a letter from Rohde, accompanied by a bill.

Dear Miss Berry,

   Please do not drink before you come to my consulting room. I've got a bad back and if there were no-one on the premises, it would mean I'd endanger myself, helping you up. You may not be aware of this, but you made amorous advances towards me. You effectively pulled me onto the floor and I sustained yet another musculo-skeletal dislocation.

I wrote back a humorous letter which he did not find amusing:

Dear Dr Rohde,

   Do you think Rhett Butler sustained a musculo-skeletal dislocation when he carried Scarlett O'Hara from the flames of Atlanta?

*   *   *

Private Eye produced a cruel and evil cover the week after R.M. died. It showed a close-up of his burial on the Mount of Olives. One pall-bearer had a caption coming out of his mouth saying, 'Here lies Robert Maxwell'. The next pall-bearer had another caption which said, 'He lied everywhere'; another said 'All twenty stone of him'. A caption from the body read, 'You're All Fired'. The other captions were even worse.

   I suggested to Dr Ratner, my doctor and personal friend, that we should turn up at the offices of *Private Eye* unannounced and descend on Ian Hislop, the magazine's editor. R.M. had always called him 'Pigslop' and his former partner, Richard Ingrams, 'Mr Wigwam'.

   Ratty felt as strongly as I did about the cover. He too was a friend of R.M.'s so he came willingly and without argument.

   The offices of *Private Eye* were filthy. They looked like the

116

contents of a Third World shack. In the front office was a secretary/receptionist manning an old sixties switchboard. The walls were peppered from top to bottom with photographs of staff parties with Hislop occupying the limelight. In the fridge, which I was invited to open, was a jar of apple juice with a floating fungus on top of it.

The secretary was pleasant and sympathetic when Ratty and I walked in, saying we wanted to speak to Hislop on urgent business. He called himself William Cartwright and I called myself Natalie Klein.*

'Do please take a seat,' said the secretary. The only seat available was a sofa, which had seen better days, with a large hole in the middle from which springs could easily cut through someone's clothing and go straight up their anus. In the corner of the room was a pile, about seven feet high, of old issues of the magazine, with coffee stains and cigarette burns on them. Half empty cups of coffee lay on chipped occasional tables and on the floor.

'May I ask what you would like to discuss with Mr Hislop?' asked the secretary.

I was waiting for this.

'Yes,' I said. 'I was a cleaner on the *Lady Ghislaine* on Maxwell's last journey. I know how he died and he didn't fall accidentally, nor did he deliberately take his life, nor was he pushed. There was another woman with me,' I added vaguely.

The secretary took a gulp of coffee.

'Perhaps it would be more appropriate to pull the Maxwell team, rather than disturb Mr Hislop who's got to go to a funeral this afternoon.'

I was intrigued by the expression 'pull the Maxwell team'. Consultants use a similar phrase in hospital casualty departments. If a patient's heart stops beating, they say, 'Pull the crash team'.

'What does "pull the Maxwell team" mean?' I asked.

'It means – send for the Maxwellologists.'

---

*Natalie Klein: The heroine of *Never Alone with Rex Malone*. I worked hard on Natalie whom I presented as an eccentric, man-crazy, passionately loyal thug. Don't ask me if she's modelled on me. If you do, you'll get a pretty dusty answer.

'Maxwellologists? Are they people who have graduated in Maxwellology?'

The woman finished her coffee and said, 'They are the only people who can help you.'

'No, I want to see Mr Hislop personally. Besides, it is likely that these people are out at lunch. Mr Cartwright and I are anxious to speak to Mr Hislop ourselves.'

Ratty was sitting on the damaged sofa, reading a book describing the history of *Private Eye*.

'A fine binding,' he remarked, smiling at the secretary.

'Yes, isn't it? I'll try Mr Hislop's line again.' This time, it rang. Hislop answered the phone.

'You can both go up now. You'll have to keep it brief, otherwise he'll miss his funeral.'

I struggled to keep a straight face. I was quite calm because I had taken some Valium half an hour before. I went into Hislop's office and hurled vitriol at him, which I am not allowed to print in this book

Soon after this came yet another incident in which I became involved to defend the honour of the Maxwell family.

A woman named Lolita Lee, who called herself a spiritualist, wrote a grossly unpleasant article in a tabloid newspaper about a conversation she was alleged to have had with R.M. from beyond the grave. Throughout, she stressed that he appeared 'chilling' and 'evil'. She made the mistake of allowing the newspaper to print her picture above the article, and foolishly allowed the newspaper to print the name of the town in which she lived, enabling me to find her telephone number.

I rang her up at midnight, a time which I assumed was inconvenient for her.

'Are you Lolita Lee?' I asked.

A sleepy voice answered, 'Yes,' which reassured me I had disturbed her sleep.

'How much is that newspaper paying you for that utterly disgraceful article you wrote in it today?'

'That's none of your fucking business! Leave me alone!'

Was this fear?

I pressed on.

'Do you know what they did to witches in the seventeenth century?'

'No.' (Why didn't she hang up? Was she intrigued by any chance?)

'I'll tell you what they did to witches in the seventeenth century. They burned them alive,' I shouted.

'In the first place, this is the twentieth century. Secondly, I am not a witch; I am a spiritualist.'

'Do the two not come from the same family? You also know perfectly well that the dead do not have the power to speak to the living, and the living do not have the power to speak to the bloody dead! How dare you call a dead man a crook when a British law court never found him guilty! I bet you screwed a bomb out of that filthy rag.'

'Maxwell *was* a crook.'

'Oh? In the light of what I've just told you, you're not, I suppose?'

'Who the hell are you anyway?' she said.

'I only spill my name to people I respect, and that doesn't include a charlatan who gets money playing on your clients' superstitions and then calls someone else a crook.'

We were both taking off. It was like the fencing scene from the film *Theatre of Blood*.

'Are you a man or a woman?' she yelled. 'I can't tell with a voice like that.'

'A woman, you odious old bag!'

The woman gave me a smattering of R.M.'s physical and psychological faults and I returned her fire with a barrage of invective.

'By the way, how old are you?' she asked. 'You sound like a sex change of about eighty.'

I ignored this and returned to her article in the newspaper which had a deeply upsetting effect on the entire Maxwell family.

'You don't think I'm for real, do you?' I shouted. 'I'll give you one warning and one warning only. I know where you live. If you upset any member of the Maxwell family one more time, I will send some thugs to your house and have you duffed.' (These words were spoken in spontaneous rage. I was a bit embarrassed afterwards.)

I love a good blockbuster, particularly in R.M.'s honour, whether it be with a seemingly intelligent man of letters or a wench using the coarse language of the gutter.

One would have thought that circumstances would improve as

the weeks passed, following the loss. In fact, I was able to tolerate the first few weeks quite well, occupying myself by seeing my friends, and going to the cinema. My arm was still out of order so I was not allowed to go back to work. Instead, I started to write this book.

8

Because of the libel laws, I will not give the name of my employer, the consultant physician who wilfully harmed me. Nor will I name the hospital concerned, nor the department. I will refer to the consultant throughout as 'Dr Beria'.

Before I heard of R.M.'s death, when I was accounted for by witnesses as being in a very 'disturbed' state, Dr Beria had shown signs of being in love with me. I had been working for him for five years and because he was particularly nice to me, and complimented me on my appearance and my efficiency, I liked him and stayed overtime every night to complete the large workload.

When he saw me working overtime, he would say, 'Oh, bless you, dear!' He always addressed women as 'dear' when trying to chat them up, which shows how inordinately common he is.

Dr Beria was born and bred in a provincial west country town and was a spoilt only child. Beria fancied himself as a ladies' man which, because of his physical appearance, was inappropriate. He was approximately five foot five inches tall and walked around in soft shoes so that he could creep up behind his staff to make sure they were working.

From the front, he looked like a weather-beaten old bulldog with leathery skin. A pair of hideously unfashionable glasses was jammed on to his face, making his looks even less prepossessing, but, astonishingly to his credit, he had large brown eyes which gave a false impression of sensitivity. In profile, he looked a bit better, with a modicum of masculinity. Although his nose looked as if it had been damaged in a street brawl, it had some character and was vaguely aquiline in shape.

Mrs Beria, his mother, was a professional dancer who spent much of his childhood working, and as it seems he had no father around the house to discipline him, his spoilt streak, perpetual desire to be pampered, and his pathetic yearning for attention, must have manifested themselves in him before he could walk.

Dr Beria loved his mother but was probably petulant when she had to leave him to go to work. It is known by psychologists that when only children become adults, they can assume that they are sent by Providence to delight and be pampered by the opposite sex, and be regarded as being more important than others.

Such a specimen was Dr Beria. I was not intuitive enough to recognize his two-faced personality, his spite in manipulating his staff behind their backs, his oily, artificial charm, his cowardice, caddishness and frequent rudeness, directed particularly at timid young nurses who feared him, and in particular at Irish women. He used to make fun of the fiery Rita Cassidy until one day she terrified him with her awesome temper and he was polite to her ever since.

I was told by almost everyone in the department that Dr Beria was 'sexually attracted' to me. The work I did for him was excellent and he used to leave notes on my keyboard saying, 'Super work, – very well done!'

My first meeting with Dr Beria was unusual. I had been sent to work in another hospital on a Monday morning and had been turned away because I had been double-booked. I then had orders to go straight to Dr Beria's hospital and report to him personally. I went to the manager of his office, out of breath and in a bad temper.

'I've had a terrible morning,' I said. 'I've been sent to see Dr Beria.' I no longer cared whether I'd be sent away or not. My spirits were low although *Never Alone with Rex Malone* had just been published (by Harraps Columbus).

I saw a strange-looking man slumped in a swivel chair, doing nothing. I assumed he was a mental patient.

'Where is Dr Beria?' I asked.

The figure struggled to sit up straight. He looked somewhere in his 40s.

'I am Dr Beria,' he said in a breathy quiet, classless voice. 'Aren't you making rather a lot of noise?'

I shook his hand, introduced myself and agreed to be taken to my office. It was a nice, homely, attic room with natural light blazing in through a big window.

Two weeks had passed. I had done a big job for Dr Beria and because I wanted to stay there I made sure I did it well, and checked it repeatedly. I left it on his desk, together with some new pens, pencils and rubbers, which I noticed he had a poor supply of. I took his empty coffee cup from his desk, tidied his papers, locked his office door behind me and got on with my other work.

The next day, Dr Beria came to his office to check his work. Then he rang me and asked me to go and see him. I assumed he was going to tell me that I was too slow so I made sure I was on my best behaviour. I knocked on the door of his office and he called me in.

'You wanted to see me, Dr Beria?' I said.

He raised some papers in front of me.

'Yes. Please sit down. Is this your work?'

'Yes, Dr Beria. Is it not all right?'

'It's not a question of it not being all right. It's absolutely superb.'

He was smiling. I smiled back. I confess to having developed some affection for him.

'Thank you, Dr Beria.'

I was wearing white denim trousers and a blue and white striped T-shirt.

'Oh, love, don't you look swish!'

'Indeed? Why do you say that?'

'You've got your sailor suit on again, I see. Superb! Superb!'

'Thank you, Dr Beria,' I said. 'You will have to excuse me now. I must go back to my office because I have to get on with my work.'

I walked towards the door, flattered but confused. Dr Beria half raised himself from his chair.

'I hope you will be staying with us for a long time,' he said. (I noticed his pronunciation of 'us' as 'uzz', the only verbal betrayal of his west country origins.)

'I sincerely hope so, Dr Beria. After all, the devil you know is better than the devil you don't.'

Dr Beria looked at me with an almost demented expression on his face and his eyes began to fill with tears.

'Oh, my dear, you're not a devil!' he breathed. He sounded like a male version of Marilyn Monroe.

'You must excuse me now, Dr Beria, my telephone is ringing and it could be for you.'

At 9.00 o'clock every morning I shared the lift with Dr Beria. Our offices were on the top floor. The lift was slow but, because I found it too tiring to walk up three flights of stairs, I went up with

123

Dr Beria. Each morning the conversation between us was roughly the same.

'Oh, my dear, don't you look swish!'

'Oh, Dr Beria, you are too kind!'

Although R.M.'s origins were far humbler than Dr Beria's and his suffering more tortuous, R.M. would never have been common enough to use words like 'dear' or 'swish'. He would have been more likely to say 'smashing' because he never aspired to belong to a more sociologically exalted social rank than his position at birth.

Dr Beria, on the other hand, posed as an educated aristocrat, causing junior doctors to snigger into their hands and other consultants to ridicule him behind his back. Nurses hated him because of his sarcasm and secretaries because of his rudeness. I was exempt from these discourtesies and had great affection for him because he liked my work and looks and always showered me with flattery.

It was my third week working for Dr Beria. We were coming up in the slow, graffiti-spattered lift. There were two nurses in the lift besides Dr Beria and myself, talking about knitting patterns in South London accents. Neither was pretty and their faces were unpainted.

'Good morning, Dr Beria,' they both said cheerfully.

Dr Beria ignored their greeting and turned to me.

'What's your surname, Eleanor?' he asked. I was surprised he didn't know it already.

'Berry.'

His voice became even more obsequious and I was sure he knew the answer to his next question before he asked it.

'I take it your family are the Berrys who used to own the *Telegraph*?' Although he asked affably enough, I was not liking the conversation and shifted from one foot to another.

'Yes. That's right,' I said abruptly. 'They've still got shares in the paper, though. How do you know all this about my family?'

'I only have to read it in the *Sunday Times*. I'm not prying or anything,' he said apologetically.

'I don't take the *Sunday Times*,' I said coldly, 'or indeed any other of Rupert Murdoch's newspapers.'

For no apparent reason, Dr Beria suddenly gave his familiar look of a man who had just had his face slapped. I couldn't understand why he looked so upset. Maybe it was the abrupt tone of my voice.

'It's a cold day. I'll soon have a nice cup of coffee ready for you,

Dr Beria,' I said. After all, I wanted to keep my job.

We got out. The two nurses fixed me with a hostile stare which I returned. This was not my first impression of ill-feeling in Dr Beria's department.

I shared the office with a raunchy girl called Karen (surname withheld). She always wore a white blouse and a tight split skirt showing her flesh up to the thigh. Her hair was thick, dark and curly like a gypsy's. Her voice was very girlish and her accent down-town Croydon. She and I had in common a love for Russian literature and Russian folk-songs which we discussed during breaks.

Dr Beria did not take long to notice Karen's down-town Croydon accent which made him feel he could talk down to her, although he used to ogle her bare legs as she walked down the corridor, and gaze at her lily-white cleavage.

Dr Beria was never rude to her when I was in the office because he was too much of a coward.

When I came back from lunch, Karen was subdued and red-eyed.

'What's the matter?' I asked.

'Dr Beria came in and shouted at me when you were out.'

'Why?'

'He rushed in and said: "Give me three sharpened pencils and a clean rubber! That means immediately if you wish to stay here! Well, don't just sit there staring with your mouth gaping open like a cretin's! You're not deaf, are you?"'

'I will not be spoken to like that. I'm walking out of here,' said Karen.

She walked to the door and put on a tailored raincoat and picked up her bag and umbrella. Dr Beria ran after her shouting like a madman. His white coat flapped behind him. It was too big for him and looked ridiculous. He chased her as far as the entrance to the underground station.

'I'm so sorry, Karen, I get these funny turns sometimes. Oh, dear, don't be upset. Please come back!'

Karen did not want to lose her job. She came back to work.

She was also sex mad. She was fornicating several times a day with a junior doctor on Dr Beria's firm. The young doctor was not unique in hating Dr Beria who patronized him in front of patients on ward rounds. He and Karen found fornicating-ground in the hospital hard to locate, but their mutual lust always enabled them to find somewhere in the end.

In the mornings, they used Dr Beria's lavatory and although the bizarre consultant sometimes forgot to pull the chain, they were undeterred and reached screaming climaxes, unheard except by me, as our office was next door to the lavatory.

A few hours later, they used a telephone box outside the mortuary and were said by passers-by, working in the hospital, to be making enough noise to wake the dead.

It was when they chose Dr Beria's desk in his absence on one of his Harley Street afternoons, that they got into trouble. Dr Beria's two private patients had cancelled so he had come back prematurely.

'There is a time and a place for everything,' he said mildly. 'I feel this is letting down the firm.'

Karen was sacked. Dr Beria didn't have the guts to sack her himself and asked the Administrator to do so on his behalf.

It did not take long for five years to pass by. A lot of staff members resented the fact that Dr Beria favoured me above the others. He said my services were invaluable to the department, and better than those of other members of his staff.

Sometimes, when I was alone in the office, he came in and threw all the air in his lungs into a breathless, Natashaesque* 'Hi!' dragging his lips from ear to ear in a creepy, village idiot's grimace.

The people at the receiving end of his sarcasm and rudeness disliked and resented his courtesan behaviour towards me. He was always offering to carry things for me. Sometimes, he would say, 'You're a real star!' in front of the people he patronized. His obvious unrequited love for me embarrassed me and caused my colleagues to dislike me even more. But because he was so affectionate towards me, it was hard for me not to like him. In a way, I felt like the Victorian actress, Madge Kendal, when she was with the Elephant Man.

One morning, I brought him his coffee. He looked odd, but not much odder than usual. He was talking down two telephones at once. I could tell that his wife was at the receiving end of the

---

*Natasha: Heroine of *War and Peace* (Tolstoy) – lively, vivacious and innocent when a child.

126

telephone in his right hand, and that his mistress was on the left-hand line. His voice became gruff as he shielded the mouthpiece of the left-hand phone.

'I won't be back before 1.00 o'clock in the morning. Put my dinner in the microwave and open a bottle of claret. No, I can't get back earlier, I'm too busy!'

He hung up without saying goodbye and spoke into the left-hand phone.

'Oh, love, my dearest, dearest love. You asked who I was speaking to. It was only the wife! It's been too long, oh so very long. If I don't see you tonight, I'll die.'

The voice at the other end must have consented.

'Oh, I'm so happy! Oh, my love, my love!'

I regretted not having taken a sick basin into Dr Beria's office that day.

I began to receive hate mail from within the hospital but my determination to find out who sent it killed my irritation. An anonymous female caller with a South London accent rang me up. She had rung several times before.

'There's a parcel for you at the gatehouse,' she said. 'I'd like to see you wearing a pair of crotchless rubber knickers.'

I collected a large brown envelope. It was addressed to 'The Boss's little sweetheart'. Intrigued, I ripped the envelope open. In it was an empty Coca-Cola bottle, a handkerchief smothered with dark pink lipstick, some loose salted nuts and a used tampon. I showed all this stuff to Dr Beria who was baffled but not curious.

'Next time the woman calls, put her straight on to me.' I told him she had rung before and that she would only be likely to make these calls to another woman. I advised him to answer with a woman's voice.

'I can have a jolly good try!' he said, raising his voice two octaves. I thought this was witty and charming and laughed.

'Let me make you a coffee for a change, dear,' he said, adding, 'Do you know you've got the most beautiful eyes?'

I was a bit wary of the remark.

'They have always served me well, Dr Beria,' I replied.

All this took place near the end of October 1991. I got on with my work and Dr Beria continued to leave me affectionate notes to say how well it was done. The words 'Oh, my dear, you really are a star!' were never off his lips.

His love for me was claustrophobic, particularly as I did not find him attractive. I continued to work overtime and to see that his work was done to perfection. I loved the hospital and was happy there. I revelled in the opportunity to gossip with other women outside my department. We walked round the square, smoking and eating cake during breaks, laughing and joking.

I had no idea that my happiness was soon to be destroyed and my life ruined by a bitchy, spiteful little man in the form of Dr Beria, who discovered that another man, and not he, was the object of my adulation and hero-worship. I also had no idea that this doctor, whose function was to relieve pain rather than to inflict it, could change from Jekyll to Hyde overnight and sadistically kick a bereaved woman bleeding in the gutter.

Dr Beria was invariably unkind and vicious when thwarted. Perhaps he was unaware of his unprepossessing appearance. His behaviour towards me when R.M. was drowned and he became aware of our relationship, was one of the cruellest episodes of conduct I have witnessed in my life. Were he to stand next in line with the original Lavrenti Beria, from whom I have taken his name, the merciless head of Stalin's Secret Police would have seemed like the owner of a home for birds with broken wings in comparison with him.

It was Dr Ratner who first informed me of Dr Beria's hostile attitude towards my grief. A month before, he had told Ratty I was the best worker in his department. Ratty rang him up the morning after the drowning to say that I would have to be off work for a few weeks because my arm was in plaster.

'Well of course, we all expected this,' Dr Beria said, apparently very unpleasantly. 'She was abnormally disturbed when she heard the news, not unlike a mental patient. At any rate, that's what I heard.'

Ratty was disgusted.

'I think that's a pretty obnoxious thing to say, considering her loyalty to you and how hard she has worked for you, sometimes staying over until 8.00 o'clock to complete the work. Besides, you told me she was your best worker.'

There was a pause. Dr Beria could dish out sarcasm to timid underlings, but words came slowly to him when he was cornered by his equals in rank.

'That was then. This is now,' he eventually muttered, adding: 'You do know she's been crossed off the books of most employment agencies, don't you?' This was a lie. It also meant that he would not give me a favourable reference after my five years of service.

On all occasions in the past when I had returned to work after leave, Dr Beria made a point of giving the impression that he had been crossing off the days waiting for me. As soon as I came back to the office, he would kiss me on both cheeks and say, 'Ever so nice to have you back, dear!'

I returned after Christmas. The plaster had been taken off my arm. The only person who seemed pleased to see me was the Administrator who was also a nurse and who kept asking me to show her my arm. I automatically extended my right arm, every time she asked. She didn't fall for this, however, and insisted on seeing the other arm which she said was still not fit to be used. She put me on switchboard duties which I always enjoyed and which helped me to relax a bit.

Apart from the Administrator, many of the staff in the department were cold and standoffish towards me, despite my friendly overtures. Rita Cassidy said that she could have done without my relatives ringing up just after the drowning. She also ticked me off for drinking alcohol after a shock. I could have done without that but didn't quarrel with her then because I was feeling too weak. Rita herself was hardly whiter than freshly driven snow. She had an illegitimate child whose father she had known casually. What sort of life will the child have without knowing who its father is?

The atmosphere in the main office downstairs where the switchboards were, was cold and unwelcoming, but I befriended two newcomers called Mark and Justine with whom I was able to share jokes. I was always on friendly terms with Margaret Samuels, the Appointments Manager.

The morning I first saw Dr Beria again, I was made to feel so miserable that I thought of resigning. He came over to where I was sitting. He didn't say hello, ask me how I was or say he was pleased to see me, as he had before.

'Ring this number and get my son on his bleep,' he commanded.

I did as I was told but his son's switchboard didn't answer. Dr Beria went outside because he was too impatient to wait. He came back in five minutes' time.

'Come on, haven't you found my son yet?'

'No, because his switchboard hasn't answered yet.'

'Let me do it for you,' he said. 'I expect I'll get him more quickly than you can.'

'Oh, please do!' My tone was sarcastic. I don't think the bastard even noticed.

I went upstairs to see Rita. I thought she might be supportive. After all, I had always been good to her.

'Help me, Rita. We're friends, damn it! Why are all these people downstairs deliberately making me so unhappy?'

Rita stopped working and turned to me without smiling. The pupils of her pale blue eyes were like pins.

'Because they're sorry for those poor *Mirror* pensioners, I should imagine. Aren't you?'

'I've always felt sorry for the injuries and murders inflicted on Londoners by those bloody fellow countrymen of yours, but at least I've never thrown it in your face up to now.'

I rushed out, slamming the door, feeling like a South African black on a whites-only train. The Administrator saw me and called me in to her office. She was pleasant and sympathetic. I told her what was wrong and also how hurt I was on reading the papers every day and finding nothing but evil about R.M., who had never been tried in a British court of law.

'Go on home,' she said. 'I'll speak to Dr Beria. I don't think you're fit to work the switchboard today.'

'I'm paid to work from 9.00 to 5.00,' I said. 'I'm not ill. I'll be OK in a minute.'

She gave me some tea.

'This will help. Why don't you go outside and have a cigarette? Then come back and we'll have a talk.'

I returned in an even more paranoid state.

'I know there's a mass movement here to persecute me and throw me out. This hospital is my second home and the people who work in it are my second family.'

'You're talking like this because you're not well. No one's trying to get rid of you. You're a very good worker. You must go home now and come back in the morning. Have a good sleep and you'll feel different,' said the Administrator.

That evening I cheered myself up by having drinks with Ratty in Harley Street. Wolf Mankowitz, renowned for his witty biography

130

of Edgar Allan Poe, struck me as being dry-tongued, serious, but affable. I asked him if he thought there was a link between Poe's works and necrophilia.

'Lady, quit the bottle and get some therapy,' he replied.

I returned to the hospital the next day and sat down by the two switchboards. Very few calls were coming in that morning. I got out the thriller by James Hadley Chase I had brought with me, and its compulsive, gripping pace took my mind off my misery.

Dr Beria came over to me.

'Oh, James Hadley Chase,' he said. 'My favourite book of his is *No Orchids for Miss Blandish*. Since he died, a lot of other books have been ghosted in his name – at least, that's what I've heard.'

I could tell he was making an effort to be friendly but his manner was artificial as if the Administrator had had a word with him.

'Someone said Kingsley Amis ghosts his books,' I said.

Dr Beria turned off the charm it had been such a strain to muster. He walked out of the room.

When my arm was better, I was moved back into the office I had shared with Rita, the office in which I had heard about R.M.'s death. The sun was beaming in which cheered me greatly and I felt my troubles were behind me.

'I'm sorry about what I said the other day,' said Rita.

'So am I.'

'I really didn't mean to hurt you. It just came out.'

I cleaned my screen by spitting on it and wiping it with a cloth. I turned the machine on and got it ready.

'OK, OK,' I said. 'It's all right as long as you don't do it again.'

'I just don't understand why you went over the top like that. Maxwell wasn't even related to you.'

'I reacted like that because I was in love with him. I don't want to talk about the subject any more. Try to remember, I am not made of iron. Besides, I've got a lot of work to do and I want to get on with it.'

Two weeks passed by. I had become on fairly good terms with Rita, and she, Doris and I used to go drinking after office hours. Doris had formerly worked for Dr Beria but found him so repulsive that she went to work in another department.

Once I had settled down, I became a new person. I got on with Dr Beria's work and made sure it was done to perfection. I visited all my friends in the hospital during tea breaks and was cheered up by them.

Dr Beria continued to ignore me. If he left something for me to do, he did so having made sure I was out of the room so that he wouldn't have to speak to me. My disdain for him increased but, as long as I did his work perfectly, I thought there was nothing he could do to hurt me.

My wellbeing was short-lived.

It was 11.30 on Friday 14 February 1992, St Valentine's Day. Dr Beria came quietly towards me, giving me one of his false and almost toothless smiles.

'May I have a word in my office, my dear?'

I said nothing but did as I was told. I had no idea what was happening, only the knowledge that Dr Beria was obsessed by Robert Maxwell and as he was Head of the Directorate, I would have to put up a heroic fight to win.

A woman from personnel, a tiny little woman in glasses from Newcastle, sat in a chair next to Dr Beria behind his desk. The seating arrangement was designed to intimidate me but I had R.M.'s spirit burning within me, and a locket with his photograph in it round my neck. I sat down opposite the ridiculous-looking couple.

'So what's all this in aid of?' I asked confidently but not aggressively.

'I am worried about you, Eleanor,' said Dr Beria.

I looked at him defiantly.

'If you waste your time worrying about me, might I suggest that your other worries must be somewhat remote?' I said.

The woman spoke. She looked like something out of *Li'l Abner*.

'Dr Beria *likes* you!' she boomed in a strong Geordie accent.

'Why have you called me in here?' I asked.

'Dr Beria's worried sick.'

I raised my eyes as if talking to a couple of nuts.

'Why?'

'Because he thinks you have a psychotic illness,' said the tiny little woman.

'I didn't know he was a psychiatrist.'

'He thinks this because you don't relate to people in an appropriate manner.'

'I'd appreciate it if you would generate your statement in a more palpable vernacular.'

'I don't understand what you said.'

Christ! The woman didn't even understand English!

'I meant, back up your statement with evidence. I find this rubbishy witch-hunt a ludicrous waste of time. I have a lot of work to do and would appreciate it if you would let me get on with it. To whom have I not related in an appropriate manner?'

'You have been involved in a myriad of eccentric incidents,' began Dr Beria, as he took off his glasses and wiped them genteelly on a handkerchief.

'I defy you to name one of these incidents,' I said.

'Your exhibitionist abuse of the tannoy system is one of them.'

'All right, give me an example.'

'Your voice sounds like the Gestapo at the very best of times. You were put on tannoy duty, the week before you injured your arm,' he began. 'You failed to realize that the tannoy is automatically broadcast all over the dialysis wards, where patients sometimes hover between life and death.'

'Well, I never!' was all I could think of saying. 'You're talking as if I had said something indecent.'

'It was far worse than that. I was tending to a patient, when I was knocked sideways with embarrassment.'

'Oh? What embarrassed you?'

'You were ranting with a Hitlerian rasp. Your exact words were, "A dented old Polish Lada has been abandoned outside the mortuary. I have had disgusting language thrown at me by staff working for five different firms of funeral directors. Would the owner of this vehicle kindly remove it, immediately."' He continued, his voice raised, '"The hearses are unable to gain access to the building, to pick up the bodies!"'

'That motor belongs to you, Dr Beria. It was your fault that the hearses were kept out.'

'That's not the point. The word "hearse" is simply not mentioned in the hearing of seriously ill patients. In any event, my car is neither old nor dented. I've had it for two months. To get back to the point, no one refers to hearses on the tannoy system.'

'Hearses exist, Dr Beria, and there are occasions when they have to be mentioned. Had you been considerate enough to park your car on a meter, this incident would never have occurred. Besides, my eardrums were almost perforated by the staff working for the five funeral directors. They taught me a few new words. I can't tolerate screaming, foul-mouthed undertakers.'

Beria wiped his forehead with his handkerchief, and leant forwards, clasping his hands.

'This incident is further evidence that you are incapable of relating to people in an appropriate manner.'

'This is outrageous!' I shouted. 'The hearses weren't able to pick the blasted bodies up, all because of you.'

'It was your use of that word,' he repeated.

'What else could I possibly have called them – slow black, shiny vehicles of doom or use rhyming slang and called them "gypsies' curses?"'

'You have a reputation in this hospital for being somewhat eccentric,' said the woman.

'OK, so I'm eccentric. Why shouldn't I be eccentric?' I said aggressively. 'I am an exceptionally hard and loyal worker. The fact that I'm eccentric is neither here nor there.'

'The British don't tolerate eccentricity,' said the woman.

'I *am* British!' I shouted.

After a long silence Dr Beria spoke.

'I believe you're very unhappy here. You are emotionally disturbed.'

I rose to my feet and leant over the desk, pointing my index finger at Dr Beria.

'Dr Beria, I have served you for five years with loyalty and dedication. You told someone I was the best worker you'd ever had. I have pandered to your requirements, such as making you coffee whenever you wanted it. I have worked overtime almost every evening to do your work to perfection.

'The answer is, yes, I am unhappy, I am unhappy because I am hurt. In the past you welcomed me back to work every time I had been on leave. "How are you? Nice to see you back? Are you better?" These words were forever on your lips.

'This time, all you did was order me to get hold of your son without even saying please.'

I noticed his hangdog expression. He lowered his head so that his forehead was almost touching his desk. He blushed like a flighty débutante.

'But I've never actually been rude to you, have I?' he asked pathetically.

'Not half as rude as you are to timid Irish nurses who are too frightened to answer you back, but rude enough.'

'When was I rude?'

'I can give you an example. I passed you in the corridor yesterday morning and said, "Good morning, Dr Beria". I didn't hear so much as a blessed murmur!'

'I didn't hear you. Otherwise, I would have said good morning.'

'It's not only that. You've been deliberately avoiding me. Outside in the square, you turn and walk in the opposite direction when you see me. You leave your work in my office when you know I'm elsewhere. You shirk contact with me and make it obvious you don't want me here.'

Again, the haunted hangdog expression, the blush and the moist eyes.

'Eleanor, I called you in because you are ill. I'm offering you two weeks' sick-leave.'

I wished I'd taken it but I wanted to protect myself with an image of selfless industry.

'I'm not ill and I'm not taking two weeks off!'

'You're ill in mind.'

'How the hell do you know?'

'Let's face it. Your reaction to Robert Maxwell's death was pretty abnormal.'

'That was because I was in love with him,' I said, adding, 'What abnormality lies in human grief? You've no idea how much that man meant to me!' I continued, 'My reaction to his death and the horrifying nature of it, was normal and totally understandable. You'd have to be as hard as stone if you can't accept that.'

'No normal person would grieve for a man like that,' said Dr Beria.

'Do you mean a greater and better-looking man than you?'

He repeated his hangdog stunt. These words must have upset him. He *must* have been jealous of R.M. He wore exactly the same expression as he had when I had gone to his Harley Street rooms to discuss my impending return to the hospital.

'I understand you were very upset by Robert Maxwell's death,' he had said.

'Yes. He was a lovely man.'

He had stared at me as if he had been bitten in the private parts by a rat. It was then that his jealousy was confirmed in my mind.

He continued to vent his envy of R.M. on me.

135

'When you were told that Robert Maxwell was dead, you asked one of the consultants to go out and buy you a bottle of whisky.'

'That's a bloody lie.'

'I was told you started a fire that night.'

'Mindless fabrication, Dr Beria, and you know it!'

'You did start a fire. The matter was reported. You nearly set the whole building on fire. You can't go round starting fires just because someone's fallen out of a boat.'

'I've had enough, Dr Beria,' I said. 'You've tried to break my spirit but you have failed. By the time I've reported this outrage to the Board of Governors, you'll be ruined!'

Dr Beria faked calmness. 'I understand you actually tried to ring up the Queen,' he said.

'Which Queen do you have in mind, Dr Beria?'

It is true that I tried to ring up the Queen (when the worse for wear), to complain about the joke about R.M.'s death that Prince Andrew made at the American Embassy.*

'I don't see what all the fuss is about,' I said. 'It was only a short local call.'

Beria finally looked as if he could take no more. He was like a bull about to die at the end of a fight.

'I've got to teach my students now,' he said to the personnel woman. 'Will you take over from me?'

'Don't worry. I'll be able to handle her.'

'I need a cigarette,' I said when Dr Beria had gone. 'May I smoke in here?' She said I could. Once I'd lit up, I felt more relaxed. The tiny little woman moved to another chair on my side of the desk.

'What exactly was the deceased to you?' she asked.

'I loved him because he was kind to me and asked for nothing in return. He was also very attractive. He was my hero and my friend, and dead as he is, he is still both those things.'

The woman looked at me as if I had come from another planet.

'Did you have an affair with Robert Maxwell?' she asked, leaning forward in her chair like a ghoul ogling a circus freak.

'That's none of your fucking business!' I shouted, but when I

---

*I considered the 'joke' made by Prince Andrew at the American Embassy to be inordinately obscene and even I do not wish to write it down.

realized what I'd said, I felt I had to change the wording, to save my skin.

'Sorry, what I meant was, that's none of your *accursed* business,' I said in a calmer tone.

I had no idea what she wanted out of me and, she was beginning to alarm me. She stared at my eyes. Nobody has ever stared me out in my life. Even on trains, I have gone to anything up to ten stations beyond my destination to outstare someone looking at my eyes.

Her eyes, peering into mine from behind her round glasses, were small, blue and piercing. I was determined not to avert my gaze. We stared at each other for at least five minutes until she finally backed down and broke into a bemused smile.

Perhaps I daunted her. Whatever the position was, she ended the interview. We left Dr Beria's dingy office and went out into the corridor. Because I had shouted at her and used the F word, I felt obliged to compliment her by remarking on the 'beauties' of her home town.

'Ah, yes, you recognized my accent, didn't you?'

'That's right. What's going to happen to me now?'

'You'll receive a letter or a phone call next week sometime, summoning you to a disciplinary hearing in the offices of Personnel.'

'So I'm to be disciplined because I loved Robert Maxwell more than Dr Beria. This reminds me of Henry II turning on his former friend, Thomas à Becket, for loving God more than him.'

'Not having heard of either of these people, I can't comment on your remark,' she replied.

Christ! Didn't this woman go to school?

She flounced off without saying goodbye in her white, clattering stilettos.

I heard nothing further the next week. I assumed that it was not against hospital regulations to have been upset by R.M.'s death, and that nothing was going to happen to me. All my friends, including my family, were convinced I was in the clear, but to cover myself, I consulted a solicitor as well as my father who offered to turn up at Dr Beria's Harley Street consulting rooms to confront him.

A month later, my telephone rang. The caller was the union representative from NALGO of which he was Branch Secretary.

'Dr Beria's complained that relations between him and you have irretrievably broken down and he wants you moved into another department,' he said.

Dr Beria engineered my move to a department where one person after another was being made redundant because of government cutbacks. My redundancy soon came up, and as he would have wished, Dr Beria could not be legally charged with dismissing me since he had only had me transferred.

Following Dr Beria's treachery, I broke down and was clinically depressed for several months. I believe in the words 'an eye for an eye and a tooth for a tooth'. Better still, an eye for a tooth and a limb for an eye. I do not wish to state the extent to which I punished Dr Beria, or indeed whether I punished him at all. Perhaps I did. Perhaps I didn't.

Ratty did, though. His articulate words blasted Dr Beria to pieces at a crowded medical conference. Dr Beria was reduced to tears and put many of his slides in upside down. It was a hollow victory for me, but a victory nevertheless.

During his repremand, Ratty had accused Dr Beria of 'peremptorily sacking her when she was grieving, of kicking a sick woman when she was bleeding in the gutter, and of being a despicable cad'.

9

CONCLUSION

There has been much morbid speculation about Robert Maxwell's death. One fatuous theory is that a Mossad agent got out of a launch and climbed onto the yacht and murdered him. Why on earth would a representative of Mossad want to kill a man who was so devoted to the Jewish people and helped them so much?

Another equally silly suggestion was proposed, namely that someone on the yacht pushed him into the water. Had they done that they would have pushed themselves out of a cushy job.

A third theory expressed in the press was that he committed suicide. Robert Maxwell would never have entertained the idea of suicide. Besides, he was a very vain man and had he died by his own hand, he would have put on his best clothes instead of falling into the water half naked. Has it never occurred to anyone that drowning is probably the most painful death of all? Doesn't anyone know what it feels like to swallow water the wrong way? On many occasions he expressed the view most vehemently that suicide was the ultimate cowardice. He was also reported to have been in a very cheerful mood during the last few days of his life, so the notion of suicide is *out*! I am convinced that he died in the following manner.

He went out to the back of the boat to be sick. Vomit was found in his throat at autopsy. (Incidentally he was also suffering from cirrhosis of the liver. That speaks for itself.) His left hand (he was left-handed) was severely mangled which means that he not only accidentally fell off the boat, he put up an enormous struggle to get back on to it. Because of his poor sense of balance caused through lack of oxygen to the brain, he must have fallen. Also to be taken into account is the fact that the rails on the back of the boat only came up to the level of his lower stomach. I am convinced that that was the cause of his death and would be prepared to bet any amount of money on my theory.

The first thing that comes to mind when thinking about Robert

139

Maxwell's complex character is Dr Samuel Johnson's two essays on the 'Whisperer' and the 'Roarer'. The Whisperer is presented as being sly, two-faced and slippery. The Roarer is described by Dr Johnson as making a lot of noise, sometimes inadvertently causing trouble and fundamentally blustering in a generally benevolent sense. The Whisperer is 'more dangerous than terrible'. The Roarer is 'more terrible than dangerous'. Even someone of low intelligence would know which of these applies to R.M.'s personality.

Robert Maxwell was not like other mortals, although curiously his was quite an easy head to access. His personality and conduct were unique. His manner in relating to others was unusual. Spiritually, he stood apart from others. His right hand did not know what his left hand was doing and because of that, few knew him entirely. I think I knew and understood him, although I don't think he knew himself.

When family life no longer afforded him the relief he sought from his black thoughts, he threw himself into projects pathologically, like a junkie, his psyche wrecked by hideous memories. R.M. identified most with the opera *Don Giovanni* but it was not women he conquered; it was companies, newspapers, football clubs and anything else he could get hold of.

There were some Heathcliffian elements in him. He was capable of intimidating and boorish behaviour towards other men, particularly effete young men with little drive, who courted his daughters. If such men met R.M. when he was clouded by Slavic gloom, he tended to terrify them and they never returned to the house. Strangely, he often said that I myself was terrifying!

On the other hand, his inordinate kindness and generosity, seeking nothing in return, was unique, extraordinary and legendary.

He was intolerant of fools and of anyone who couldn't make him laugh. His sense of humour lifted his Slavic glooms and made him playful and childlike. He enjoyed horseplay, practical jokes, pinching women's behinds, clicking their bra straps and annoying people by throwing rubbish out of car windows, and bathing-suited women into swimming pools.

He loved things of simple beauty such as ballet, the fragrance of flowers, the crispness of mountain snow, the chirping of small children and music which never appeared to bore him. He liked flamenco dancing and beautiful young women in brightly-coloured

140

clothes with roses in their hair. He also liked girls who were aggressive, cheeky and courageous. Towards those he cherished, his love knew no boundaries.

Readers of this book may have gained the impression that I regard Robert Maxwell as a saint. If they have, they have been misled, but because of the tenor of the book, I cannot blame them.

Like any of us, he was no saint. He was a very lonely man and even his wife, family and friends sometimes failed to exorcize the demons within him. The barbaric murder of his family during the war cast a weighty and unlifting shadow upon him. No doubt his secret shame of having been afraid of his tyrannical father, contrasting with the Rambo image he showed to the world, haunted and isolated him. He often said he was going to write a book about loneliness one day.

I have never thought of him as being a happy man which could be an explanation for the most singular manner in which he related to his staff.

Contrary to superficial and unfair reports, there was no cruelty in his being. He was honourable and fair and had a heart of gold. Because of his unusual voice, his sudden and overbearing demeanour, added to his overpowering sexuality (concentrated sex oozed from every pore of his person when he wasn't too overweight), he had an ability to terrify people to shaking wrecks.

Since his death, terrible things have been said about him in the press because the cowards who wrote about him knew he was no longer there to hit back. Even the Judge presiding over the trial of his sons Ian and Kevin, remarked emphatically that newspaper coverage about him had been 'grossly offensive'. He was not the evil crook he was made out to be – certainly not to the extent his tabloid persecutors were. They blackened his name for financial gain and had no regard for the psychological harm they were doing to his widow and children.

The public forgets that he only had two years' formal education and no training in accountancy. It is known that the Board of Trade published a report, so-called, in 1969 or 1970, stating he was 'unfit to be at the stewardship of a publicly quoted company', owing to a misunderstanding about the sale of a few encyclopedias. Had he intended to deceive, why was he not arrested? Why was he not jailed? The answer is that there was no evidence that he was a fraud or a crook.

I do not profess to know anything about high finance, but any unbiased, fair person would tell us that he made hasty decisions in moments of euphoria and could be cavalier in his judgement. I agree, he was reckless, but my reason for saying this has nothing to do with money. He actually allowed me to drive his beloved Ghislaine, having been told I had smashed up someone's car only the day before!

He told me once he was a schizophrenic and he may have been right. When he reverted to the child, Lajbi, and in many ways the Lajbi side of his personality prevailed over the Bob side, there were moments when he acted impulsively, without regard of consequence.

I don't think he had a mature understanding of money once he had made it, what to use it for or where to put it. This is not an uncommon trait in individuals who have raised themselves unaided from dire poverty to riches.

The affair regarding the *Mirror* pensioners could be another example of the disordered side of his personality and of his rapidly-progressive terminal illness. We tend to take oxygen for granted. When someone has emphysema and oxygen is not properly supplied to the brain, that person cannot act rationally. Even his speech was distorted towards the end of his life. He referred to monkeys as 'minkeys', and sea as 'tea'.

On 29 May 1991, a document was signed, apparently authorizing the transfer of well over 400 million pounds from the *Mirror* pension fund. This is not a subject I understand but I am sure that if he acted unlawfully, his medical condition prevented him from being aware of it. Perhaps in a fit of cavalier optimism, when he again reverted to the Lajbi character, he assumed he could repay the funds in better times. He had always paid back what he borrowed and did so with interest. He would not have taken it without intending to return it, and was not tried by a British court of law where you are innocent until you are proved guilty.

* * *

So far, I have not touched on the significance of the mismanagement of the *Mirror* pension funds. I have not yet mentioned the appalling effects it had on the pensioners themselves, irrespective of whose fault it was.

Some people think I don't know how the other half live and suffer. They are wrong. I bloody well do. There have been times in my life when I have been happy, and other times when I have suffered far more than I have allowed others to know.

I admit that I have been fortunate enough not to have been penniless, street-bound or destitute. I have never had to beg or turn to prostitution to avoid starvation. If I live to old age, it is unlikely that I will be pensionless and living in doorways.

The idea of someone who has slaved all their adult life, reaching old age with nothing to live on in return for their labours, is more than unjust. It is horrific beyond belief. An elderly person would in many cases, be too infirm to queue in job centres, having retired, seeking work to pay for living expenses. I have been approached on countless occasions and told that I know nothing of the perils of poverty. I haven't had to endure it but I still know what it is like. Yes, I do come from a wealthy newspaper family but I know what poverty is because I have witnessed it.

My guilt about my background is painful, but my selfishness has prevented me from giving assets away. My guilt has prevented me from wasting a single day of my adult life. Since I graduated from University with a 2.2 in English, I have forced myself to work 35 hours or more a week, and be so exhausted by Friday that I have slept through most of the weekend.

I have often imagined leading such a life until the age of 65 and facing no more than a vacuum because of the deprivation of my pension. Before I worked full-time as a writer, I worked for 30 years, starting as a translator, using French and Russian, and as a verbal interpreter (a failure in this instance, as I lost my head and couldn't stop shouting while interpreting). I have also worked in nearly all London's hospitals, often doing overtime. Friends of mine have remarked that my life-style (if not my assets) was similar to 'that of a member of the working classes'. When I worked in these places, I disguised my strange brogue and spoke with a bogus Irish accent, to hide my origins. It did not take long for the Irish accent to come naturally, no matter who I was speaking to.

'Oh, I do wish you'd stop speaking with that dotty Irish accent!' said my paternal aunt irritably, as she sat at an oak table, pouring tea from a Meissen tea-pot.

During those 30 years, in which I tried to prove myself, I saw people from different creeds and walks of life, all of them trying to come to terms with their own suffering. I saw people from broken homes, escaping from violent, drunken husbands and fathers on graffiti-strewn, vandalized council estates. I saw people who were blind, deaf and physically handicapped. Most of all, I came into professional contact with the mentally ill, incarcerated in cripplingly depressing hospices in the rougher parts of London.

I write all night, as I find it easier, and sleep in the afternoons. I go to an office where I work as an Agony Aunt, two mornings a week. I answer letters from sufferers from depressive illness, and I am sure my letters help them and elevate their moods.

I hope if anyone accuses me of being uninterested in the shattering plight of the *Mirror* pensioners, they will take the trouble to read my words. Yes, I do know what poverty is. I also know what mental illness is because I've suffered from it. I am a manic-depressive, and this affliction is about as close to poverty as you can get. I alternate between being a loner and a compulsive puritan, and being outrageously wild. Sometimes, I am euphoric. Other times, I feel I am at the bottom of a well from which there is no escape. The alarming thing about the condition is that my mood swings very suddenly and without warning.

I've seen starving children on the backstreets of Marseille and given them food. I have seen freezing beggars on the streets of Dublin and taken them to department stores where I have bought them winter clothes. I have spent time talking to dossers on London streets, given them money, advised them to be more aggressive with housing authorities, and instilled optimism in their hearts.

Yes, I do know what it is like to be old, penniless and too tired and ill to earn. I also know what it is like to be sacked from a job, after five years' devoted service, for the crime of loving someone who had loved me. I know what it is like to be called names, to be pilloried and to have had someone spitting in my face, while others have stood around me, laughing and leering.

What happened to the pensioners was as horrifying as it was monstrously unjust. Why blame me, though? And why blame Robert Maxwell whose brain had ceased to function normally? Having said that, I shudder on thinking of the bleak, hopeless, later years of respectable people who had slaved like navvies, since leaving school or college. I cannot think of a more Dickensian plight, devoid of reward for exhausting toil.

I defy anyone to insult me by saying I am indifferent to what happened, that I am indifferent to human suffering. I've seen it all and I've felt it all. I feel it all the time. Perhaps those who reproach me imagine that I am happy. Some of the time I am not, although neither happiness nor unhappiness are static states of mind.

On a lighter note, I can give an example of the behaviour of one particular *Mirror* pensioner. I was puzzled by his appearance in the *Evening Standard*'s 'Londoner's Diary' column. He had complained that he could no longer afford to heat his swimming pool at his holiday home in the south of France. When Robert Maxwell was a child, he didn't know what a swimming pool was, heated or otherwise. The only bathing facility available to him was a polluted river, shaded by trees and bitterly cold, even in the summer. I had often rung newspapers up to complain. My call to the *Standard* was answered by a certain Anthony Cheeswright, a friend of my family.

'Oh, God, is that you again, Eleanor?' he said.

The depressive phase of my manic-depression is brought on by my justified suspicions that I am not valued for what I am. Often, I am not seen as a writer, a listener to the problems of others, one with the gift of bringing laughter and optimism to those in need. I have been regarded, by a lot of undesirables as 'just an affluent newspaper magnate's daughter'. Young men pursued me in my youth, to gain an introduction to my father, hoping to get jobs on his newspapers through the 'old boy network'. This was always after the sex act, not before, in case my father turned them away. After that, I was of no further use to them. My father's gardener's daughter, a child of my age, told me she only pretended to like me and forced herself to play with me because she was living on my father's land. Countless others, though despising me, have indulged in my goodwill and generosity. The cruel words 'You're lucky you're able to *afford* to take me out to dinner' have all too often been thrown in my face.

And yet R.M., whose childhood was about as destitute as any child's could be, gave me every inch of his bear-like love. He embraced me and moved me to tears by saying, 'Many only want you for your assets. I'm not like that. I value you for what you are.'

In July 1979, at the wedding celebration of R.M.'s daughter, Christine, a cruel, odious politician lammed into me, unprovoked.

He was Peter Shore* (now dead), who looked more like a mangy, floppy old dog, bundled in from outer space, than a human.

R.M. introduced me to Shore in front of an audience of about 100 people. As he always did, he told the puzzled, befuddled creep about my achievements. Unfortunately, he told him about my father's trade, as an addendum.

'Oh, come on, Bob!' said the Nasty Piece Of, 'Surely you can do better than introduce me to the daughter of a shit like that!'

It would have been beneath me to use violence against this man, in front of R.M., although I wanted to slap his face. I shan't be laying any orchids on *his* grave. I said, 'You don't get any medals for hitting people below the belt, Mr Shore, or votes either.'

I was so upset that I decided to punish Peter Shore and punish him I did. The only person who knows what form the punishment took is my psychoanalyst.

I am not naturally vicious or vindictive, but I hold burning and vehement views about inviolate loyalty towards loved ones, and unprovoked cruelty, whether it is delivered to me or other people. I take inordinate trouble to ensure that tormenters are punished. Some say it should be left to God to punish the wicked, but I don't believe in him, so I do so myself. Sometimes I can understand why the Kray brothers believed in revenge. If Sir Winston Churchill had not believed in revenge, we would now be living under Hitler's and Eva Braun's grandchildren.

My beloved father had been publicly dishonoured, so only an appropriate form of revenge was good enough to punish Shore, and I am proud of doing what I had to do although I didn't enjoy it.

I am born under the sign of Taurus. When the spikes are driven into my shoulders, I don't back off or slump in the dust. I go for the picador's stomach and do not flounder until his heart, lungs, liver and intestines are spattered over the ring, before the swooning crowds.

---

*The late Peter Shore: He was allocated a life peerage in 1997 and was known as 'The Rt. Hon. Lord Shore of Stepney'. Among other things, he was Labour MP for Stepney from 1964 to 1974 and Secretary of State for Economic Affairs from 1967 to 1969. During Margaret Thatcher's long period as Prime Minister, Shore was a shadow cabinet minister.

My maternal aunt, the gypsy and famous writer Eleanor Smith, felt as I do. Unfortunately, I never met her. She died before I was born. Like myself, the honour of loved ones was paramount to her. She did not believe in an eye for an eye and a tooth for a tooth. She believed in an eye for a tooth and a limb for an eye.

I am a public-spirited person, so I enjoy inflicting pain on sadists. I enjoy it because I know I am protecting vulnerable parties from being treated in the same way.

I learnt a lot about the human race since R.M.'s death. My views are perfectly encapsulated in Gogol's words, quoted later at the top of Anecdote 12.

*   *   *

I have read Nick Davies's book which was published shortly after R.M.'s death, and find his conclusions about R.M.'s character to be very different from my own.

He says R.M. called him to his bedroom when he was in bed with a cold on a rainy Sunday afternoon. Davies says R.M. was 'suicidally' depressed and wanted to 'jump out of the window and end it all'.

Those unaware that the human mood is not static, probably regard this incident as evidence for his decision to end his life. Sufferers from colds are always depressed on rainy Sunday afternoons and they don't necessarily kill themselves.

Davies tells us of an implausible incident occurring in Paris, concerning an argument between R.M. and Betty about an overcoat. He is said to have got into a bait because she told him he would get a cold if he didn't button it up. Davies said R.M. told her to 'fuck off'. He would never have spoken to her like that, although he often got very bad tempered when she fussed over him or gave him advice about his health. I asked Betty whether R.M. had told her to 'fuck off' and she denied it.

As for the allegation that his children virtually trembled at meals when he was present, I never noticed any such instances, and I had lived at Headington Hill Hall for a considerable amount of time. On one occasion, Christine's twin sister, Isabel, said something to her father about Turgenev (the Russian writer), pronouncing the name incorrectly. Her father confronted her, his mouth full of steak, and ticked her off for not pronouncing the name right.

147

'Do you have to be so awful, Daddy?' Isabel retorted, piqued. 'I don't know anything about Russian literature, do I?'

Was this fear?

R.M. told Ghislaine that her dress was indecent and Ghislaine picked up a bowl of strawberries and threatened to empty it over her father's head.

Was this fear?

Kevin, aged about 16, called across the table to his father: 'Is the Honourable Member for Buckingham still capable of rising?'

The author of such a remark could not possibly have been feeling frightened. There were repetitive reports that R.M. 'bullied' and 'terrified' his wife and children. There were a few times when I saw him startle them and cause them to be temporarily subdued, but they nearly always retaliated. Had he been cruel to them, as his father had been to him, they would not have grown into uncomplicated, mentally-stable adults. They are cheerful, level-headed and devoid of signs of disturbed personality.

If the signs of the zodiac are to be relied on, R.M. was a Gemini. I believe he may have had a split personality and could have done certain things and forgotten about having done so. When he was looking after me during my illness, he stated he had schizophrenia, but this may have been said to put me at my ease.

He was a born-again religionist who took his beliefs seriously. Would such a man have knowingly ruined other people's lives? A lot of financiers on the *Daily Mirror* were corrupt and so were the bankers connected with the pension funds. I suspect that they, and not a man with an oxygen-deprived brain, were guilty, but there again, high finance, like engineering, is a subject I know nothing about. In this book, I have only sought to examine Robert Maxwell's character, personality and unforgettable role of kind and intimate friend. Further, the memory of his widow Betty's kindness towards me over so many years, is something I shall cherish until I am laid in earth.

10

Anecdotes

1. Robert Maxwell, a Disgruntled Yorkshireman and Eleanor Berry

I came into Bob's office one morning during one of the campaigns I was working for him. He had a man in there with him. I knew who the man was but I didn't speak to him because I did not like the look of him. I'll hand it to him that this was not his fault, but I definitely wished to avoid any verbal exchange with him all the same.

Bob pointed at him, abruptly, using his thumb,

'Do you know who this man is?' he asked.

The atmosphere in the room made me nervous. I wanted the man to go away. I never speak gently or quietly when I get nervous. I bark.

'I haven't the faintest idea who he is,' I shouted. 'Does he work in your garden?'

Bob laughed and turned to the man.

'She doesn't mean to be offensive. She's just very shy.'

The man was irritated and spoke with a heavy Yorkshire accent.

'Shoy? Shoy? Bluddy abroopt, I'd say!'

It was Arthur Scargill.

2. Robert Maxwell Wins Challenging Battle to get Eleanor Berry out of Bed in the Mornings

I lived with Robert Maxwell for a year. For a man with a short fuse, he bore my incommodating habits stoically and patiently.

During the General Election campaigns, everyone moved into the Wharf House, overlooking a stagnant canal near Bob's Buckingham campaign offices.

I was not all that industrious and spent the mornings in bed, sleeping. Occasionally, I was stirred by the sound of vigilant campaigners, calling 'Vote while you can. Maxwell's your man!' over loudhailers.

The Maxwells had an Irish cleaning woman. I think her name was Mrs Mock. I was unaware at the time that Bob spent a lot of the mornings in the house. One morning, I was rumbled. From 8.00 o'clock onwards, I was woken at fifteen-minute intervals by Mrs Mock's shrill Irish accent.

'Mr Maxwell says it's high time you were hopping out of your bed. He thinks you've been there quite long enough.'

150

I ignored her visits. At 12.30 the great man himself rattled into the bedroom. He came up to me and sat on his haunches like a policeman asking a motorist whether he has been drinking. He leant forwards, his face less than a foot away from mine. I was struck by the extreme sweetness of his breath. He pointed vehemently, first at me, then at the ceiling. For some reason, I suddenly thought of the film *A Clockwork Orange* which I had recently seen. A quotation from it came into my head.

'Leave us be and I'll be right as dodgers for this after!' I said. He appeared irritated.

'You! Up!' he shouted.

I knew the game was up for me. I obeyed. After that he made me sleep on a camp bed in his study.

This was not unpleasant. I woke up very early each morning because the bed was so narrow.

I used to watch him working at his desk, without his knowledge. He was sitting in profile. He often wore his tie loosened at the neck when he worked alone at a desk. This was something which set my blood on fire. I loved to lie there and look at him, and the thing which excited me most was the fact that he had no idea that he was being watched.

The experience was similar to the thrill of a naturalist observing a fierce wild animal which thinks it is alone.

3. Fear

I was doing my A-levels during the year the Maxwells very kindly said I could stay in their house, free of board and lodging. I had been thrown out of the YWCA because I had sent the Communist Party round to its odious proprietress as a practical joke.

Sometimes, after dinner, Bob gave me some secretarial work to do. This was easy because all his letters were short, although he dictated quite fast and I couldn't keep up with him.

'For Christ's sake, slow down, Bob!' I shouted, suddenly.

He waited for about a minute, before he spoke. I noticed that he looked excited, puzzled and startled at the same time. He looked me in the face, smiled a bit strangely and then tilted his head backwards, in his 'I don't know whether I'm angry or turned on' pose.

'Are you OK, Bob?' I said.

He stared into space as he spoke.

'I know others have told you this, before,' he said.

'Told me what?'

'You are without doubt a truly terrifying human being!'

'Oh, come now, surely not.'

I shall never forget these words. They have haunted me to this day. Whenever I meet a man I like, I try to treat him like Dresden china.

4. The Man in the Yellow Tie

I went to stay in the Maxwells' house at a later date. I was at University then. It was 1974, at the time of Watergate. Bob and I were sitting in the kitchen, reading *Pravda*. The editorial was worded in such a way that we were both in stitches. So scared was the Soviet Government of Nixon's apparent insanity, that the newspaper's editorial ended this way, in bold capitals.

PRAVDA THINKS THAT THE AMERICAN PEOPLE ARE BEING VERY RUDE AND VERY UNKIND TO THEIR BELOVED PRESIDENT.

'At least Nixon's another person with a truly terrifying personality,' I said.

Bob's eyes became glazed as if he were in another place, a place which saddened and disturbed him.

'That's right ...' he remarked, and laid an emphasis on the word 'right'. Although he was still sitting at the table, his mind was elsewhere. I was not intrusive enough to ask him his thoughts.

'How long can you stay?' he asked.

'How long would you like me to?'

'The longer the better.'

'I'd like to stay for about three more days, if that suits everyone else.'

'It does,' he said, abruptly, adding, 'There's a little job I want you to do for me.'

'Which is what?'

He gave me the name of a man living in Newport Pagnell. I hadn't met the man. Apparently, he had had a political connection with the constituency.

'Do you want me to find out something about him?' I asked.

'Yes. Just find out whether he keeps an electoral register on the desk of his study.'

'But I don't even know his address, so how should I know where his study is?'

Bob gave me a blown-up map, showing the street where the man lived. He told me the house number.

'What if he isn't keeping the register on his desk? Supposing he keeps it in a drawer?'

'All I want to know is whether it's on his hands.'

'What's his name?' I asked.

'Sorry, I forgot to tell you, it's Rupert Taylor,' said Bob.

'What does he look like?'

'He's got very short grey hair. He's about 6ft tall and dresses ridicuously formally, even when he's not working.'

'When do you want me to go there?'

'At about 6.00 p.m. on a weekday. He lives at home. He stops his paper-work and cooks himself a meal at about that time.'

'Is he married?'

'No. He's not the kind, like I said.'

'Is that all you want me to find out for you? If I find it, do you want me to bring it to you?'

'No. Just tell me if he keeps it in his house.'

'How old is he?'

'Late fifties.'

'I don't mind doing that for you. I'll go over tomorrow.'

I left the Maxwells' house at 4.00 p.m. On my journey to Newport Pagnell, I busied myself with excuses for entering the man's house. As I am a poor map-reader, I had to stop to ask several locals the way.

At about 6.14 p.m. I went to the house. The street it was in was neat and tidy but the house itself had a shambling, tumble-down appearance.

I knocked at the door. It was opened by a man of medium height, with white hair and a crew-cut. He was wearing a dark blue shirt and a yellow tie. He corresponded with Bob's description.

'I don't think I've seen you before,' he said in a Scottish accent.

'Nor I you either.'

'Who are you? What do you want?'

I repeated the words I had rehearsed during my journey.

153

'My name's Sue Jennings. I've just been promoted to the post of Executive Director in the new community centre that's been built. They tell me you keep a register of the names of the more senior residents round here. We're anxious to find out where records of their names are kept so that we can encourage them to spend their days at the centre.'

I hoped I wasn't 'terrifying' Rupert Taylor. I had become very sensitive about terrifying men.

'You'd better come in,' he said.

He ushered me to a room divided into a kitchen and living room. A heated saucepan lay on top of the stove. I could smell a combination of beef and tomato sauce.

'Would you like some tea?' asked Taylor.

'No, thank you.'

'Sit down, would you. I'll go and find the list.'

'Thank you. I'm sorry to have inconvenienced you.'

The man went upstairs and found what I had asked for. The booklet had the title 'Electoral Register' on its cover.

'This is what you wanted, wasn't it?' asked Taylor.

'That's right.' I took the booklet and looked through it. I wondered whether it was the one Bob was asking about.

'I can photocopy all the names for you. I've got a copier here,' said the man.

'OK, then. Can you photocopy the cover as well, please?'

He walked away from me. Then he suddenly turned round to face me.

'I've reason to think you're not who you say you are,' he said.

'Oh? Why should you think that?'

'Because you seem to be interested in the booklet's cover, as well as what's in it.'

'I am who I say I am. To save you trouble, you only need to copy the cover. I can find the names in a public reference library.'

The man suddenly became hostile.

'You were sent here, weren't you?'

'Yes. By my colleagues in the new community centre.'

'You're not telling the truth.'

'Are you calling me a liar?'

'Yes. I recognize you now. I've seen you before.'

'I don't recognize you. Where have you seen me?'

'Up the Labour Hall, two general elections running. I saw you

154

operating a printing press. You're the woman who cracked all those filthy jokes.'

'This is absolutely ridiculous!' I said. 'I've never been anywhere near the place. The person you saw just looked like me, that's all.'

'I'm not stupid,' he said. 'I know your voice. You got up and took down the Union Jack from the Buckingham Town Hall, and put a Communist flag in its place. Your name isn't Sue Jennings, at all. It's Eleanor Berry.

'OK, so my name's Eleanor Berry. What's your name?'

'Rupert Taylor. At least I'm honest. You are not.'

I had no idea what was going on, or why Bob wanted to know if this man had an electoral register in his possession. I had been intrigued. Now, I was getting bored.*

'I demand to know who sent you here,' said Taylor in a hostile tone.

'I've already told you twice,' I said aggressively.

'Did Maxwell send you?'

'No!'

'Are you quite sure?'

'Yes!'

'I don't believe you.'

'You can believe whatever you want.'

'Will you please leave.'

'Not until you photocopy the cover.'

'I'm not going to.'

'It doesn't really matter. I've seen it and I know what it looks like. I won't trouble you any more.'

I left the house and got into the car. Taylor had pulled his lace curtains aside and was gaping at me. I've never liked the colours dark blue and yellow together.

For some reason, the man wearing these colours has often appeared in my dreams since Bob's death. He weeps and talks

---

*I later found out that it is illegal for anyone to be in possession of an electoral register, when an election campaign is not taking place. I do not know the reason for this law. All I know is that the man in the yellow tie had broken it. Bob wanted to know whether or not he was honest. It transpired that he was not.

about the loss of his pension although he had no apparent connection with the *Mirror*.

Bob was alone in his study when I got back to the house. I changed into some other clothes. He had already had dinner. There was a tray of cold food and a decanter of wine on an occasional table, for me.

'The answer's yes. That man does keep a copy of the electoral register in his house,' I said.

'As I thought. This incident's been all over the constituency. You fucking *terrified* that man! It's not something you said to him, specifically. Not only did you bark demands at him. You turned up at his house in *fucking* black leather!'

'Oh, come, now! I did what you asked me to do. If you'd been a woman, you would have said, "go upstairs and fetch my sewing." Then, when the order had been carried out, you would have said, "Why did you go upstairs and fetch my sewing?"'

'What the hell are you talking about? Sewing? Sewing? Have you ever seen me sitting here, sewing?'

'No. Of course, I've never seen you sewing.'

'It's a pity you took your black leather off. I would like to have seen you in it!' he said.

5. Robert Maxwell and the Typhoid Injection

I decided not to tell Betty that I was ill one of the times I visited the Maxwells. She was surprised by her husband's lateness and she asked me to accompany her to the Pergamon offices to tell him lunch was ready.

He came out of the building while I was waiting outside with Betty, and his method of greeting me was terribly friendly, as ever. He said to her, 'Why don't you ever tell me Eleanor's coming? I would be able to look forward to it!' He had uttered these kind words on a myriad of occasions.

The generous remark touched me. He was always very physical with me. Each time, he kissed me on the mouth, whether Betty was there or not.

The fact that he was wearing his tie loosened did not help matters on this occasion. I felt the same symptoms as I had had some years earlier and made the mistake of looking him in the eye. His eyes were hypnotic and locked me into a stare I could not break. Then came the giddiness and the knowledge I was going to fall.

When I came round, I failed to recognize either Bob or Betty. After a fainter comes round, his memory goes for a few minutes, and he doesn't always recognize those he knows well.

I was lying on my back on the grass, just outside the Pergamon offices. Bob was kneeling beside me. He was shaking me by the shoulders. Because I was lying down and he was kneeling by my side, and my grip on reality was still absent, I assumed automatically that he was a doctor.

For some reason, I rolled up my sleeve and asked him to give me a typhoid injection. I then noticed he was understandably not holding a syringe in his hand.

I soon knew where I was and who I was with. I was mortified with embarrassment. He continued to kneel on the grass. He leant over me, his lips about six inches from mine.

'You're ill!' he said, confrontationally.

'No, I'm not!'

'I've seen you do this before, haven't I?'

'Yes, I think you have.'

'I'm extremely concerned about the kind of company you are keeping in London,' he said obscurely.

6. Lavatorial and Gastric Problems up at the Hall

Bob thought that the younger children are when they first start to drink alcohol, the tougher their livers will become in later years. Without medical knowledge, I can't give an opinion about this, but I hold no store to it.

Since the beginning of my lengthy stay in his house, he encouraged me, in a good-natured way, to drink perhaps more alcohol than suited me. I drank to please him, just as I dressed and did my hair, to please him.

There was one thing, however, that I could not do. I have an aversion to smoked salmon. I am incapable of holding down this delicacy which delights others so much. Even if I put it in my mouth, I start retching. I cannot stand slimy, salty, slithery pink food of any kind.

Bob loved it. He ate large quantities of it and liked his guests to do the same. The first time he gave it to me, I waited for him to look the other way, and put it in my pocket. He gave me some more. I felt I had to eat it and cut it up in small pieces and washed it down with water. I realized I had to get up. The distance between the dining room and the ground floor lavatory in Headington Hill Hall is short.

When I had finished, I washed my mouth out and pulled the plug. I found there was something wrong with the lavatory's plumbing. The level of the water rose to the top and over the edge of the lavatory bowl, onto the carpet.

I spent at least fifteen minutes clearing up. I scooped away handfuls of water and pieces of thrown-up smoked salmon from the carpet into the basin and washed them down the drain. I couldn't do much more than that, so I went back to the dining room.

Every night, Bob liked me to have several glasses of wine and I was determined to conceal from him the fact that I had a weak head. There were a number of occasions when I had to get up and go out, faced with the indignity of the slow-moving lavatory cistern.

However, I was smart. I discovered an ingenious trick. This was an occasion when I had had to eat more smoked salmon. I closed the lavatory lid and knelt on it. I lifted the lid of the tank and was sick over the ballcock. I remembered to bring down a plastic bag the following morning, to clean out the tank.

On one of these occasions, I found Bob outside. He wanted to come in to wash his hands, something he did several times a day.

'What have you got in your bag?' he asked.

'That lavatory of yours, it overflowed,' I said.

'It's not a lavatory I use,' he said. 'I only come in here to use the basin. We're waiting for the plumber.'

I was beginning to feel ill at ease.

'Are you, now?' I eventually muttered.

7. Welcome to my Bath

I was doing a translation job for a firm in Oxford. The hours were 8.30 a.m. to 5.30 p.m. For a short period, I shared a flat with a woman who prevented me from using the bathroom between the hours of 7.00 and 9.00 a.m.

The Maxwells very kindly allowed me to go to their house early each weekday. I was given permission to use Bob's private, majestic bathroom. It was a fantastic bathroom. It made Cleopatra's bathroom seem like a slum dweller's in Calcutta, in comparison.

It was a cold, foggy morning. The time was 7.00 o'clock. I had a hangover and had slept badly because the woman I shared with had blared a transistor radio for most of the night. I was extremely disorientated on arriving at Headington Hill Hall.

I was astounded on seeing Bob leaving the house at 7.00 o'clock, just as I was arriving. I thought it strange for a millionaire publisher to be leaving home at such an hour and because I was barely awake, I made the following utterly fatuous remark:

'Hullo! Fancy seeing you here!'

'I live here, don't I?' said Bob.

8. Robert Maxwell, the Irishman and the Bottle of Wine (<u>suitable only for persons of 18 years and older</u>)

I was often invited to stay with the Maxwell family on weekends nearest my birthday. I always sat on Bob's right. He was in a good mood on these occasions. Everyone was laughing and joking, but during lunch a family row broke out. Ghislaine was allowed home from her boarding school at weekends. She wanted to spend the whole of Sunday riding. Bob complained that Sunday was the only day he could see her.

Ghislaine reacted and told her father not to make such demands on her. Isabel, her sensible older sister, took her father's side and accused her of being inconsiderate. The boring exchange between the father and his daughters lasted for about ten minutes.

Bob became bored and turned to me.

'So it's your birthday, today, is it? What year were you born?'

I took three years off my age as any woman would.

'All right. I'm going down to the cellar to find a bottle of wine for that year. I bet you won't be able to drink all of it in one go.'

'I bet I will!'

He left the room and came back five minutes later with a dusty bottle of red wine, labelled what he took to be the year of my birth. He opened it and teasingly put it on his left, out of my reach. I saw this as being a game and I leant across him to get hold of the bottle.

159

'Don't be so impatient, Missy!' He gave me a smack on the back of my hand. 'You can't have the wine until you've finished your champagne.'

I drank the champagne and reached for the wine. He and I struggled with the bottle which he held in a vice-like grip.

'You promised I could have the bottle of wine after I'd finished my glass of champagne,' I said.

'All right, Basso Profundo. I bet you can't drink the whole bottle.'

'I bet I can!' I repeated.

I let him fill my glass to the brim, and drank it. He filled it up every time I drained it. I went on until the bottle was empty. I felt a bit nauseated, and lost all my inhibitions.

'Christ, you drank it!' said Bob.

'You never thought I would, did you?' I said.

'No, I can't say I did. Because it's your birthday, and you've achieved this extraordinary feat, I want you to stand up and make a speech.'

I stood up. 'No problem, Bob,' I said, 'but I'll have to hold on to the chair.'

'Never mind the chair. Just make a speech,' he commanded.

'I'm now going to tell you a hilarious joke,' I said.

'Get on with it, then.'

'An Irishman went to a job centre. "Where did you last work?" they asked him.

'In a mortuary,' said the Irishman.

'Why did you leave?'

'I was fired,' said the Irishman.

'Why were you fired?'

'For bunging the corpses doon onto the slab, instead of layin' 'em gently, and after layin' 'em doon, for fockin' 'em from behoind.'

There was a silence. I looked at Ian, who was sitting on Bob's left. I looked at Bob whose appearance shocked me terribly. Mercifully, Betty did not understand the thick Irish accent I mimicked. Nor did Ghislaine. Bob turned green and was beginning to sweat. There was a mild tremor in his hands. I knew I'd made him ill but I couldn't remember exactly what I'd said.

He leant forward and with an effort, reached for a bell which he rang.

Oping, a sweet Filipino lady, who had worked for the Maxwells for many years, scurried into the room.

'You rang, Mr Maxwell?'

Bob clutched the table and rose to his feet.

'Mr Maxwell, are you all right?'

No answer.

'Mr Maxwell, do you need help?'

'I am going to my room, where I want some hot sweet tea,' he said in the voice of an out-of-work funeral director.

'Ian!' I said.

'Yes.'

'I'm afraid your father's been taken ill. He was OK a minute ago.'

'Yes, I know he was.'

'Have I upset him, in some way?' I ventured.

'Yes, you bloody well have'

'But why?'

'Don't you dare ever again talk to my Dad about necrophilia!' he shouted.

'Why not?' I asked, stupidly.

'Because it cracks him like a nut. He's just not up to hearing about it.'

'Oh, dear,' I said. 'Shall I go up to him and say sorry?'

Ian banged his forehead with his outstretched palm.

'No, no, please. Anything but that!'

'What's going on?' asked Betty, in a baffled tone. 'What's wrong with Papa, Ian?'

'Nothing. He's exhausted. He'll be fine.'

'Do you think he'll have forgotten what happened, once he's finished his rest, Ian?' I ventured.

'I should think so. The man's got other things on his mind, besides Irishmen screwing the dead,' said Ian.

I was not happy about what happened, but I was dared to drink the wine, and I have never said no to a dare.

9. Stormy Elevenses with Maxwell and Proust

I have a phobia about illness, both in myself and those close to me.

It was a Saturday morning. I was having coffee with Bob in the offices of Pergamon Press.

'You don't need five cubes of sugar,' he said. 'You'll make

161

yourself sick.'

I ignored him.

'Another thing: Take your spoon out of your cup when you've finished stirring your coffee.'

We were talking about *A La Recherche du Temps Perdu*. He was just as argumentative about the deathly tomes I had been studying at University, as he was about the sugar. I got heated about Proust's dreary protagonist, Marcel, his obsession about his bedside light and his tedious preoccupation with memories evoked by a crappy old biscuit.

'It doesn't make any sense, the boy continuously sending messages from his room to his mother's cook, just to find out whether or not his mother is coming to see him. Why the hell should a boy be concerned about whether his mother loves him? What does it matter to him whether she loves him or not? Surely, his only logical motive for passing messages to the cook, would be prompted by his terror that his mother had been *taken ill*!'

'Why do you say that?' Bob leaned back in his chair and cleared his throat. He always sounded like a gang of hell's angels trying to start their motorbikes when he did this.

'It's simple. It stands to reason. There couldn't possibly be any other explanation. A child wouldn't care whether his mother loved him. He would be worried about her imminent death. That's why the only thought going through his head would be a paralysing fear, not of rejection but of *illness*.

'At meals, he would be permanently staring at her, fearing she would collapse and die at the table. His pulse would be quick and his appetite poor. Such a boy would live in eternal hell, dreading her immediate death, not her lack of love for him!'

'Oh, bollocks!' said Bob.

10. The Sinister Parson and the Chicken

It was a Friday in late November, about three weeks after Bob's death. I went out to lunch in an Italian restaurant. A rare ray of sun for the time of year, shone through the window I was sitting by. It was warming the right side of my face.

I was pleased to see the restaurant was empty because I wanted to be alone, savouring the sun and my memories of Bob. I ordered chicken and peas and a gin and tonic.

An overweight parson lumbered into the restaurant. He was about 55. His face was red, his jaw sagging and he had tiny, watery blue eyes. He had a leering, lascivious look about him which disquieted me, even from a distance.

He came up to me and looked at me as if assessing a ten-bob knock. If the *News of the World* is anything to go by, it is common among men of the Cloth to have an eerie, off-putting randiness about them.

He sat down opposite me and looked at me from the corner of his eye. His hair was parted halfway down his head to hide his baldness.

'You don't mind me sitting here, do you?' he asked. He had a hearty P.G. Wodehouse accent which sounded rather common.

'I do mind. Every table in here is free. There are plenty of other places where you can sit.'

He ignored me but stared at my eyes. His eye contact was intrusive and a little chilling.

'How dare you stare at my eyes like that!' I said.

He continued to give the patronizing smile of an ageing roué who thinks any woman will automatically attach herself to him like a limpet.

'Your eyes are peculiar. The irises are so dark one can't see the pupils.' There was something unpleasant about his tone.

'One can also take a long walk along a short jetty during a tempestuous winter's night, for all one cares,' I said.

'You're in black, I see.'

'Go away and leave me alone.'

'Are you in mourning?'

'Yes. I thought I told you to leave me alone.'

He smiled again and leant across the table. His teeth were brown and his lips moist.

'If you give me the name of the person who's died, we can sit here and pray together.'

'You're harassing me!' I shouted. 'I'm not a believer and I've told you to leave me alone. Piss off!'

A mini-skirted waitress, aged about 20, came to the table. He stared at her in the same way as he'd stared at me. He pointed at her legs and said, 'I say, nice pair of pins! Does your boyfriend like you in mini-skirts?'

163

She ignored his vulgar advance. 'I've brought you your usual sir, steak, spinach and chips.' My order came next.

'You chit of a girl! Can't you remember I have fish on a Friday?'

'Sorry, sir. We have Dover sole ready. Would that suit you? I forgot about your Friday lunch being different.'

'Yes. All right, then.'

As she went into the kitchen, he pinched her behind and was subdued by her failure to react. She came back with the Dover sole and put it on the table. I had already started eating. My thoughts and memories about Bob had been interrupted and the pale sun had disappeared behind a black cloud. It started to rain.

'I'm going to say grace,' said the parson. 'All you have to say is Amen. You don't mind, do you?'

'Keep all that to yourself and don't impose it on others. I wish you'd go and sit somewhere else.'

The parson said grace in Latin. I ignored him. I picked up my chicken in my right hand, as my left arm was still bandaged. I suddenly felt Bob's spirit within me. I ate the chicken in a bestial manner, as he sometimes did, and stretched across the table to dip it in the sauce.

'I must say, I don't think very much of your table manners, young lady,' said my unwelcome companion.

'How the hell do you think St John the Baptist ate his chicken in the wilderness?' I shouted.

11. The Sotheby's Auction of Robert Maxwell's Possessions (see the central panel of The Haywagon by Hieronymus Bosch)

The auction room that bleak Friday afternoon was a cesspit of gluttonous, gloating riff-raff. Cynics and hate-filled hooligans lurched like unfed vultures to get a closer view of the degradation of a dead man unable to defend himself or his property. These animals pushed each other out of the way, like necrophiles desperate to get to the body first before violating it.

I was pleased to be there because my presence proved that I am not a coward. As a beacon crushed against by a toxic wave of sickening moral decomposition, I almost felt Messiah-like, trampling on a sea of brain-corroded felons.

'Let me through!' I shouted. 'I knew the man. You did not.' My words were quoted in the *Investors' Chronicle* (the February 1992 edition), but the lad who wrote the article* did not know my name. I felt like getting up on the auction stand and reciting the 'O pardon me, thou bleeding piece of earth' speech from Julius Caesar.

Sick jokes were cracked by the callous carrion crow wielding the hammer, his piteous humour blacker even than a demon's soul, inspiring sneering laughter from the leering Geinian** ghouls, carnally roused by a dead man being done down.

How strange that in *The Merchant of Venice*, the 'hero' is the one recklessly borrowing money, on the vague assumption that his ships will come home, and it is the 'villain' who is owed, instead of owing!

How curious that in Maxwell's case, the 'villain' is the one who owes the money (bugger how much)! He did not steal it. He borrowed it. He meant to return it with interest as he always did when he borrowed in the past. He did not return it this time, however. He did not return it because he died. Is someone to be blamed because they die? The Reaper comes to all of us, does he not?

Had Antonio died before being able to repay Shylock, his gilt-edged catafalque would have crossed the stage, draped with creeping blooms, amidst solemn piped music. His carved head, intricately engraved on top of what bore him to his priceless, marble sepulchre, would have been etched with laurels of gold, embossed in rubies.

Even a part of Shakespeare was immersed in the centuries-old curse. Antonio was adulated because he owed money to a Hebrew.

In one instance, the debtor is deified. In another, he is condemned. The reason behind this loathsome hypocrisy and

---

*The short entry in the *Investors' Chronicle*, reads as follows:
'A pretty blonde woman brandishing a (forbidden) cigarette, forced her way to the front, barking, "Let me through! I knew the man. You did not." – A cry which some might have considered a trifle unwise, given the number of *Mirror* pensioners in the crowd!'
**Geinian: Adjective derived from the name Edward Theodore Gein (pron. Geen), a somewhat macabre American gentleman from Wisconsin (1906–1984). (He was hardly an eligible bachelor).

moral ambiguity need hardly be explained. There is only one difference between Maxwell and Shylock. One owed. The other *was* owed. In common, they were both of the same race. There is one law for the Semite and another for the Gentile, and has been since biblical times, one law for the Jewish people and another for the golden-haired *goys* who can 'do no wrong'.

It is said that anti-Semitism no longer exists in England. Perhaps it is not seen in the living room. Try unlocking the safe. The ignorant, in their tragic, blinkered denial, might even be surprised by their findings.

'Eleanor Berry certainly does have an intense style of writing' (Gerald Jacobs) *The Jewish Chronicle*. He was referring to the above regarding the Sotheby's auction

12. Cowardice, Sadism and Redeeming Kindness

How much inhumanity there is in man, how much savage brutality lies hidden under refined, cultured politeness, and even in men whom the world accepts as gentlemen!

Gogol

The day I left the hospital, which I am not allowed to name, was one of the saddest days of my life. My services there had been praised for five years. It appeared I was liked by almost everyone who knew me, by those who called themselves my friends, those for whom I made tea, those I reduced to tears of laughter with my dry humour, women I comforted whenever they had had trouble with their men, medical secretaries whom I helped with their spelling and grammar, those who wept on my shoulder whenever Dr Beria humiliated them, ... those, those, those! Christ, a bloody eternity of those ...

I walked out of the West Wing into the square. I suddenly remembered words from one of Christine Keeler's books, 'I walked past the jeering women on entering Holloway Prison with my head held high.' I copied her.

A crowd, comprising many of the people whom I thought were my friends, had gathered in the square. To make things worse, this was a week when the newspapers had had yet another field day, referring to the *Mirror* pension funds. I like to refer to it as *1984*'s 'Hate Week'. Shouts of 'Maxwell's tart!' flooded my ears, as well

166

as '*Mirror* thief's moll! Who do you think wants you here?' Other worse insults were hurled at me. A woman, whose five hundred word post-mortem report I had once computed for her, as she had found the medical terminology too difficult and the subject matter too morbid for her genteel tastes, came up to me and spat in my face. She must have had a bad cough. Her sputum was as black as a raven's wing.

I walked past these people, smiling and waving at them. Occasionally, I twirled round and extended my arms in greeting, partly to confuse them, mainly to give the false impression they couldn't hurt me.

I saw two men leaning out of a top floor window. They were too far away for me to recognize them. One of them shouted 'God bless you, Eleanor Berry!' Those words hit me harder than the insults and spitting.

About ten people suddenly broke through the crowd and walked towards me. They were led by my devoted friend, Doris Nicholson, alas now dead. She roused my few allies into a lusty rendering of 'For She's a Jolly Good Fellow'.

Accompanying Doris and her followers was an Irish porter I had gone soft on, while working in the hospital. He was an alcoholic who had the courage to confess his vice to everyone he met. He had been given a second written warning (after a third, you were sacked) for being drunk in charge of a dead body which he was pushing along a corridor, singing 'Clang, clang, clang went the trolley'. He put his hand on my shoulder and said, 'Don't let the bastards get to you.' I would almost have preferred it if he had slapped my face.

It was the spontaneous kindness coming straight from these people's hearts, rather than the cowardly cruelty of the rest of the crowd, that completely broke my spirit. Try as I did, I could not control my tears. After muttering 'Thank you so very much' to my allies, I held my head high and walked towards the main gate of the hospital.

My union representative was standing at the gate. He held strong views about the *Mirror* pensioners and stared straight through me.

'I couldn't help you because your union fees weren't paid up to date,' he said.

Any fool would have known he was lying. When Dr Beria had

first started persecuting me after Bob's death, I tried to lessen the gravity of the whole affair by using melodramatic, theatrical humour. I went to the union representative's office and threw myself at his feet, shouting 'Help me, comrade!' He reacted to my play-acting in good humour and vowed to support me. When I had to mention R.M.'s name, he turned cold, like a summer sun obscured by a black cloud.

He was smiling secretively as I passed him. I failed to look him in the eye and walked through the gate, my head still high. I went home by taxi and lay down on my bed. I felt ashamed of being English. I wanted to die.

11

Analysis of Robert Maxwell's Handwriting

A graphologist had the following observations to make about Robert Maxwell's handwriting:

The writer is an observant, intuitive, innately intellectual person whose actions are very much dictated by his instincts. He does not appear to be someone who would allow himself to be coerced or persuaded to act against his wishes.

He is proud, independent, aloof and somewhat autocratic. His social manner should manifest poise, self-confidence and not a little egoism. There is a certain dominant quality about him and, despite what appears to be a deficiency of warmth in the way he relates to people, he probably enjoys occupying the limelight and expounding his views. One nevertheless senses a fragmented element within his personality – particularly where personal relationships are involved; as if he finds it difficult or distasteful to forge concrete bridges between himself and others.

The writer does appear to vacillate between despondency and optimism; the latter perhaps being the more pronounced trait. The handwriting does convey the impression that he has experienced some sort of serious trauma at some period (possibly bereavement, illness or a shattering disappointment), the effect of which remains with him and, at times, casts a weighty shadow. Nevertheless his resilience, tenacity and even stubbornness propel him forward and his sporadic flashes of spontaneity and enthusiasm can be infectious.

He is neither a self-pitying man nor a particularly compassionate one. There is an element of rigidity in the way in which he seems to hold tradition, propriety and self-discipline in esteem. His is a highly critical disposition, prone to impatience, intolerance and inflexibility.

The writer does not appear to be particularly interested or, indeed gifted, in a practical/technical or commercial profession. So far as it is possible to determine, his interests and aptitudes would perhaps be of a more cultural nature – conceivably with a bias towards the written or spoken word.

Whilst he does not appear to be emotionally demonstrative or particularly sentimental, he does seem to be fond of children, as well as loyal and dutiful towards those for whom he feels responsible. He is possessive and acquisitive (with people and objects) and is inclined towards selfishness and insensitivity. However, it is not in his nature to pretend to be what he is not, nor would he necessarily even consider such an act – even if by so doing, it would make others happy. In many respects, therefore, one could describe him as honest.

Like all of us, he has weaknesses and fears – but probably would not wear them on his sleeve. He should make a good friend, but a cold, belittling and unforgiving enemy. His predictability fluctuates as does his mood. He is a human being – and an ambivalent one at that; he guards his privacy and appears to impose rigid guidelines on himself and even more stringent ones on others.

There is a certain dynamic quality about the writer which even the few words so poorly photocopied reveal.

He appears to hold 'Eleanor' in esteem.

Of note is the fact that the graphologist had no idea that the handwriting sample was Robert Maxwell's.

*My Master took me from the cradle and recreated
me in his own image. – The author*

171